W9-DEW-268

FROM FLINTLOCK TO M1

FROM FLINTLOCK TO M1

WRITTEN AND ILLUSTRATED BY

Joseph W. Shields, Jr.

COWARD-McCANN, Inc.   New York

COPYRIGHT, 1954, BY JOSEPH W. SHIELDS, JR.

All rights reserved. This book, or parts thereof, must
not be reproduced in any form without permission.
Published simultaneously in the Dominion of Canada
by Longmans, Green & Company, Toronto.

Library of Congress Catalog Card Number: 54-5800

MANUFACTURED IN THE UNITED STATES OF AMERICA
BY THE MURRAY PRINTING COMPANY, WAKEFIELD, MASS.

TO MY FATHER

Acknowledgments

THE WRITER wishes to express his gratitude to the members of the Government Documents department of Howard-Tilton Memorial Library, Tulane University, New Orleans, for their patient aid and forbearance.

He is also deeply indebted to Mr. Ned Reed and Mr. Paul Estachy for access to their collections, and especially to Mr. E. W. Eley for his invaluable technical advice and the kind and generous use of his tremendous firearms collection, so many specimens of which were disassembled, examined, and used as models for the illustrations.

Contents

Introduction

A WELL-KNOWN current photograph shows an enormous artillery piece pointed skyward against the blue uneven rim of Nevada mountains. From a point which is obviously at the end of the weapon's trajectory rises an incredible mushroom cloud of chaotic fire, seething with ruin, a dreadful red pall resembling the birth—or death—of a galaxy. And somehow the whole picture has a touch of the nonsensical about it, as if the gun crew were appalled by what it had done to the landscape several miles away. It was too incongruous for belief. The gun was fired, and a relatively small act produced another of unimaginable orogenic violence. Brute force and raw power in the making, somewhat like Dr. Frankenstein earnestly constructing his own monster. It was as though a man struck a match within the safety of his own house, and a gas leak blew the house to kindling.

We have become almost inured to such spectacles through simple repetition, having seen over three dozen similar blasts fuse the earth at Alamagordo, Hiroshima, Nagasaki, Eniwetok, and Nevada. The soul-searching and worrying, the paralyzing moral uncertainty which followed the cataclysm at Hiroshima have almost ceased. In short, being unable to do anything about it, the citizen has accepted this specter as he accepts death, taxes, and the normal run of human inevitabilities. Warfare has never beheld anything like it; man can level mountains and obliterate his own cities.

Lost in the cacophonous afterblast of atomic explosions is the indistinct, puny bark of an inefficient arm, the rifle—a few dollars' worth of wood and steel, loaded with several grains of something akin to powdered celluloid, and propelling a one-third ounce missile a distance measured in hundreds of yards. It is small wonder that the importance of such a diminutive weapon, the common denominator of war, has been all but forgotten in the stupefying roar of our recent achievements.

And yet, A-bomb or no A-bomb, the rifleman is the keystone about which all military operations are constructed. Every large-caliber weapon is designed to support him, and similar enemy weapons are directed towards killing him. Why, then, should a dwarf be the target of a battle among giants?

The answer is that the rifleman and his weapon form a combination unique in all warfare. He can operate his weapon and carry its ammunition all by himself. He fires by direct observation and is the one completely self-sufficient combat team—one weapon controlled by one brain, one set of reflexes. His rifle is the one member of our entire arsenal useful to him both at the limits of human vision and at clubbing distance, in daylight and in darkness. And properly trained and employed, he has the greatest potential chance to do damage, for no one is ever closer to the enemy.

Normally, both contenders in a given war have roughly the same supporting weapons, and their use in attack and defense hinders movement and makes any advance a costly one. Fire from friendly supporting weapons in the attack is intended to reduce the enemy's fire by saturating him with high explosives, enabling the advancing infantry units to move with as little hindrance as possible. In the defense, the same weapons are again turned on enemy weapons and on his advancing troops and vehicles. The actual issue is decided by the few men whose physical location determines the limits of the front lines. If they break and run, then territory is lost. If they reach an objective and hang on, then terrain is won. Everything, including the tactical atomic bomb, is intended to enable the rifleman to move more freely by overwhelming the enemy lines with massed fire. The limits of an entire nation's power are delineated, not by how far its bombers penetrate, nor by where its guided missiles land, but by where its infantrymen are. Not until a rifleman plants his G.I. boots on a piece of soil and begins to dig in do we hold that piece of ground.

This uncompromising necessity has been forgotten time and time again, more so in World War II than any other. By 1940, machines of all sorts had been brought to an awesome level of development, and in the face of their mechanical attraction, ground fighting seemed just a little archaic. Radio commentators spieled knowingly of push-button war; tanks shot holes through one another at tremendous ranges, and every spectator of the drama settled back to watch the bombing of the German ball-bearing industry grind the Nazi war machine to a speedy halt. Somehow, the Germans failed to receive any immediate notice of their fate. By August 6, 1944, the entire United States Army had on hand in Europe exactly *one* infantry replacement to fill the gap caused by the day's casualties. We had sunk that low. So states Colonel S. L. A. Marshall, whose splendid work, *Men Against Fire,* constitutes the most comprehensive research into the entire problem. Thousands of veterans remember being pulled out of various arms of service and dumped unceremoniously into infantry training in the latter part of 1944. Contrary to the unanimous opinion of the victims, it was not a cantankerous scheme dreamed up by the Army; the infantry had been so neglected that it had simply run out of replacement troops as battle casualties and the scope of operations increased.

The drift of the matter is that rifle development is an incalculably important military issue even today, and since those armed with it do most of the dying, their need for the newest and best weapon hardly seems excessive. The rifle is not a combat relic, despite the idea, which periodically becomes accepted as dogma, that ground fighting will soon dwindle into a sort of mopping-up operation, like Arab women and pariahs cleaning up after a battle. But past events point the way to the present, and on into the future. The evidence is available for study, if only we choose to look at it. From the foot soldier's point of view, the entire history of firearms warfare may be summed up in the fact that weapons tend to hit farther, faster, and harder than those which preceded them. And it is something of this picturesque and often brutal history that we have to tell.

As the days of feudalism drew to a close, the first gunners and their weapons inherited their military position almost by default, it would seem. Certainly they were no match for good longbowmen, who could keep a number of arrows in the air at once and drive those feathered shafts through several inches of oak planking. But gunpowder was a leveler; it could reduce bastions and walled cities to toppled heaps of rock. In large weapons, at any rate, the potential existed. Though the new firearms, dismally primitive improvisations, were lamentably capricious in their operation, a man could fire one after comparatively little training; a competent longbowman was, of necessity, the product of a lifetime of practice and conditioning. Perhaps the chemical wonder of early firearms contributed to their success. In those bleak superstitious days it was agreed by everybody that gunners were in close alliance with the Devil, or at least negligent in their service of the Deity, and prowled the countryside enveloped in the cloak of death.

In any event, the passage of several centuries firmly established gunpowder arms as the standard armament of all Western nations. Yet even after infantry firearms developed into something like workable devices, their users were as much to be protected as feared. The musketeer could reload his arm in about the length of time it would take to sneak up and strangle him, and after loosing one shot which might or might not hit an object the size of a Cadillac sedan at point-blank range, he had to be guarded against the shock tactics of cavalry or any ambitious soul with a large sword. So firearms poked their black muzzles through a bristling wall of infantry spears, or pikes.

This one-time necessity fixed the role of infantrymen for the next three hundred years. Long after firearms were perfectly capable of doing the job all by themselves, cold steel was considered the only proper way of dealing with the enemy. It was a symbol, a badge of valor, which military men were loath to abandon.

The need for firearms plus spears forced the infantry into clumsy, dense formations. Safety indeed lay in numbers. And to make a virtue of necessity, troops were drilled into something resembling automatons in order to fire, reload, and wheel to always present a solid unbroken rank to the enemy. It amounted to undergoing combat while performing the manual of arms during close-order drill; and it *was* a drill, all done in synchronized moves to the signal of ruffled drums. Since every nation employed exactly the same principles, battles were usually won by the most highly drilled and stubborn troops, those who could best retain their formations (and hence their striking and defensive power) no matter what the enemy was doing to them. By the early 1700's the bayonet had replaced the pike, enabling every man in the formation to bear a musket, with a corresponding increase in fire power. But the tactical pattern had been set; close order, volley fire, naked steel, and banners were the hallmark of European war, a system which reached its zenith in the chorus-line uniformity of the Prussian troops of Frederick the Great.

Such was the level of military development towards the close of the eighteenth century. What was to follow, no one could even guess; the system which dominated Continental wars was to run into the damnedest enigma it was ever called upon to face, an army of untutored colonial amateurs whose very ignorance was the key to their salvation. In fact, their success went far beyond their original intentions and expectations, and in winning the war they created a form of government which today stands out among some of its contemporaries like a bright seashell in a matrix of slime.

Here was something new under the sun; a mere colony broke away from its mother country and lived to tell about it. The times and the locale were ripe for it, of course. The country was tremendous and separated from its rulers by three thousand miles of open sea. It had no single brittle seat of power; its very diversity gave it an elasticity under stress possessed by no European nation.

The revolt certainly could not have happened under a feudal system, all castles and lords, and serfs and huts. A rebellion in the Middle Ages, had it occurred to anyone, would have been smashed like a bug against a windshield by troops of armored cavalry. During succeeding centuries the feudal lords were broken, one by one, across the knee of the king, and power migrated from diversity to centralization. The sole blessing of feudal wars was that they had been fairly small. But under kings who could enforce obedience from all their dominions, wars became bigger, and hence more expensive. The day of a few mailed horsemen, a host of retainers, and a mob of ill-trained foot soldiers, was done. Successful warfare under a king who was in complete control of the show required artillery, professional armies, immense payrolls, prodigious supply facilities, and more taxation.

This surfeit of taxation, used to finance endless private dynastic wars and borne by those who had the least to gain by the expenditure, became intolerable to the spirit of freedom which had begun to sweep, almost impalpably, but like a clean wind, across the face of the eighteenth-century world. The formation of this nation required a special set of circumstances, a change in world conscience and, indeed, a special set of weapons. For the governed had to be armed with a killing power equal to that of their rulers. Had it not been so, the colonists might have faced the British ranks with the hopeless bravery of East Germans throwing rocks against the slab-armored, invulnerable sides of Soviet T–34 tanks. Though firearms and our way of life were definitely not hatched out of the same egg, they formed the basis for its possibility. Our weapons are tightly woven into the fabric of survival; in a sense, our nation staked its fate on their capabilities. This being so, they should be the best obtainable. And so often they are not.

For the American soldier has been lauded as the best-equipped, the healthiest, most intelligent, and best-cared-for soldier in the world, which he is. His training, health, morals, and sanitary facilities are watched with a keenness which other nations regard as overindulgence. What is often overlooked, with hardly a murmur of protest, is the fact that he has sometimes been among the most execrably armed. By 1840, his weapons were a full quarter-century behind the best European arms; in the Spanish-American War, he was an absolute millennium behind the rest of the world, being armed, for the most part, with a single-shot black-powder relic that was expected to stand against the smokeless-powder Mauser magazine rifle.

His issue machine gun and automatic rifle of today were designed during Woodrow Wilson's administration; his service pistol, when William Howard Taft was in office. For something of a comparison, one has to picture a modern air force equipped with Flying Jennys or Sopwith Camel aircraft. Even the M1 rifle, superlative weapon that it is, was conceived in the days of noodle-shaped flappers, bathtub gin, and raccoon coats, all before the market crash of 1929. One suspects that simpler designs, lighter alloys, and more rapid fire have appeared in the meantime.

The one area where most of the fighting takes place is still governed by the most obsolete arms in our arsenal. This, notwithstanding the fact that small arms are the cheapest of all weapons to manufacture. The most powerful of our European bases will be worse than useless if they are overrun by enemy troops. And those bases, if held at all, will be held from the ground. Somehow, the one inexorable aspect of warfare seems to be that groundfighters, and the weapons they employ, will be with us for some time.

The Background of Rebellion

THOUGH the existence of United States Government-made shoulder arms does not predate 1795, the story of firearms began sometime in the first half of the thirteenth century. One night a monk, a shaven-head alchemist, was busy in his candlelit cell, pondering questions whose answers may forever evade mankind; and there, amid the flickering lights, he mixed Nitrum of Memphis, used for the first time in its pure state, with sulphur and burnt hazelwood. Suddenly there occurred something the like of which western man had never seen, heard, or felt before—an instantaneous visible blast of heated gases, a cloud of stinking smoke, and a thunderclap, like the entrance of Satan himself. Forces of a power far beyond that of human muscle or bow strings had, with astonishing rapidity, been brought into the world.

Deterred not in the least by the astounding consequences of his work, Friar Roger Bacon experimented further and at length wrote down the formula of his mixture, concealed in a now-famous Latin anagram. The secret of Bacon's success, if the demolition of one's laboratory can be classified as such, lay in the fact that he had learned to obtain pure saltpeter by dissolving the raw material in water, heating it, and allowing pure crystals of potassium nitrate to form through evaporation. His explosive mixture, seven parts of saltpeter, five parts of charcoal, and five of sulphur, was black powder, essentially as we know it today.

Undoubtedly the Chinese knew of gunpowder long before the Christian Era, perhaps as far back as the time of Moses. A passage from their ancient Gentoo Code of Laws reads as follows: "The magistrate shall not make war with any deceitful machine, or with poisoned weapons, or with cannons or guns, or any kind of firearms." But for practical purposes, China might have been another planet, and the appearance of gunpowder in Europe must rank as a separate discovery.

It is the date of application of gunpowder, not the age of its existence, which made it such an important factor in world history. That date will never be known, exactly, and he who first thought of utilizing expanding gas to propel a missile on some directed course is buried under the dust of many centuries. However, by 1320, military firearms were fairly well known, and though woefully ineffective, began to edge out the more conventional weapons. Their use was deplored, of course. It was quite proper and Christian to spit a man on a lance, or cleave him with a broadsword, or smash his skull with a mace, but gunpowder . . . no; clearly an invention of the devil. In view of what happened, maybe they were right at that. Eventually the practical side outweighed the ethical side of this stirring moral issue, and firearms lost their identity in their function and became accepted as part and parcel of warfare.

The earliest guns were metal tubes, open at one end to receive a charge of powder and a solid projectile. The propellant inside the gun was connected by a small vent to a shallow depression in the top of the barrel. The depression was filled with priming power and was ignited by hand with a slow burning match. It was almost worse than no gun at all; the poor gunner had to support the gun, keep the muzzle pointed towards the target, and apply a lighted match at the same time. However, the design of something as potentially murderous as firearms could not be held in check for long, and they underwent rapid improvement and alteration. Over the years it was decided to put a flashpan, to hold the priming powder, at the side of the touch hole, and fasten the match to a cock mounted on a transverse pin in a slot in the gunstock. The lower end of the cock or serpentine protruded through the bottom of the stock, and served as a crude trigger. Pulling the trigger back pushed the serpentine forward, and rested the sputtering match against the priming powder.

This matchlock, while an improvement over the crude hand cannon, was no great shakes for efficiency either. The match had to be kept lighted, would not work in dampness, and betrayed its position at night. It had long been known, however, that iron pyrites and steel would also produce sparks, and that seemed to be the best method of attack. In Nuremburg, in 1517, this line of experimentation produced a weapon known as the wheel lock. In this system a notched steel wheel was wound up against spring tension, like an alarm clock. A piece of iron pyrites, held in the vise jaws of the serpentine, bore down against the wheel, and when the trigger was pulled, the released wheel revolved against the pyrites, showered sparks into the powder-filled flashpan, and discharged the gun.

It worked beautifully, but who could afford it? None but the extremely wealthy, who ordered magnificently wrought specimens, inlaid and carved into works of art, and used them primarily for hunting. The military service could not use a weapon so heavy, delicate, expensive, and complicated. The need for a better weapon resulted in a much simpler design, one in which the sparks were produced by a blow of flint against steel, rather than by rubbing pyrites against metal. The early form of this weapon, called the snaphance, is traditionally believed to have been invented by Dutch fowl poachers, who could not afford wheel locks. Professional limitations prevented them from carrying the light-producing matchlock, and in an effort to make crime pay, they invented the flintlock. The original form, the snaphance action, employed a hammer whose jaws held a piece of flint, and a sloping piece of iron, called the battery or frizzen, located above the flashpan. When the hammer was released by pulling the trigger, it swung forward; the flint glanced against the frizzen, threw sparks into the pan and fired the weapon. The snaphance lock required that the pan cover, used to protect the powder from the elements and spillage, be opened by hand prior to firing.

It was subsequently improved, after several developmental steps, into a form in which the pan cover and frizzen were combined in one unit. The blow of the flint against the metal frizzen served the dual function of creating sparks and opening the pan cover to receive them at the instant of firing. In its final form, this weapon, the flintlock, lasted up to the middle of the nineteenth century.

At the time of the American Revolution, the flintlock represented the highest form of firearms development. The war was fought in large measure with smoothbore flintlocks. The art of rifling gun barrels had been practiced for several centuries, but the rifle, though enjoying vast popularity in the Colonies, unfortunately occupied a secondary place in the Revolution.

As far back as the early 1500's, some unknown craftsman, probably of the Nuremburg school, discovered that by engraving spiral grooves on the inside wall of a gun barrel, he could improve the weapon's accuracy. The bullet, gripping the rifling, was forced to rotate about its own axis as it traveled down the barrel. Once free in flight, the bullet continued to spin and tended, throughout its unequal fight against gravity, wind, and air resistance, to maintain its original direction. But the European rifle was a primitive affair and remained so for hundreds of years. To load it, one had to drive the lead ball down the barrel with an iron ramrod and a hammer. The bullet became deformed under this violent treatment, and powder residue left in the barrel after each shot made the succeeding shots increasingly difficult to reload. After various attempts to use it for warfare, the major European powers abandoned it almost entirely.

This monstrosity, almost unchanged (except for the lockwork) since the sixteenth century, came to America in the hands of a group of Germans and Swiss who settled in eastern Pennsylvania. These people came from the only area in the world where the rifle was used in any quantity; it was only natural that they should manufacture their native weapon. In spite of all its defects, the rifle had one potential advantage that the frontiersmen and gunsmiths could not forget—it was accurate, at least more so than the smoothbore musket. Improvements were made, a few at a time. By the middle of the eighteenth century a new rifle had evolved. This completely American weapon was the Pennsylvania or Kentucky rifle. In its fullest development it was a long slender rifle with a heavy octagonal barrel about 40 inches long, stocked in curly maple or other native wood, and embellished with brass decorations. The lock was usually a European import, since it was cheaper and easier for the gunsmith to buy the manufactured article than to make one. The rifle's accuracy and effectiveness was due to a loading procedure involving a lubricated patch. The defects of the European rifle centered, remember, about loading and reloading. With the Pennsylvania rifle, such difficulties were greatly alleviated. In the buttstock of each rifle was a small box with a hinged cover, containing a number of greased linen or leather patches, each cut to the same size. The rifle was loaded by resting the butt plate on the ground and holding the muzzle upward. A measured amount of powder was poured into the barrel from a flask or horn. A greased patch was placed over the muzzle, a cast ball laid on it, and started into the bore with the thumb. A wooden ramrod was used to slide the ball, enclosed in its patch, down the barrel until it came to rest against the powder charge. The patch filled the grooves in the rifling, causing a tight fit between ball and barrel and acting as a temporary gas seal. This obturating effect boosted both pressure and velocity. The higher pressure resulted in increased recoil, so most frontier rifles used a bullet less than half the weight of that used in the military smoothbore musket. This, in turn, allowed the rifleman to get along with less lead and powder, both scarce commodities in the wilderness. The rifle was, of course, somewhat slower to reload than the smoothbore, a fact which made little difference to the frontiersman. With a flintlock weapon he could get only one quick shot at game in any event, so he willingly traded speed for long range accuracy.

The military musket was a different animal entirely. As wilderness con-

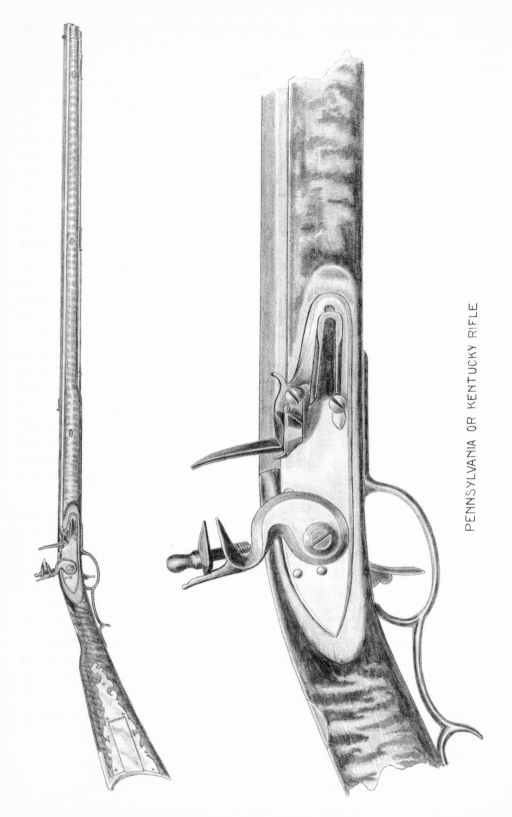

PENNSYLVANIA OR KENTUCKY RIFLE

ditions determined the ultimate form of the rifle, so continental warfare impressed certain requirements upon the weapons used in settling quarrels between nations. For some time the European wars had employed large closely-grouped formations of men. The early military firearms were dreadfully inefficient and were exceedingly slow to reload. Since the infantrymen were completely vulnerable after firing their weapons, each troop formation contained men armed with pikes or spears, to stand off cavalry charges or attacks by hostile infantry while muskets were being reloaded. Such formations were self-defensible only when they resembled a hedgehog; this meant packing men in close formation. Later, the invention of the bayonet allowed the infantry to fend off cavalry unaided. But by that time a whole military tradition, difficult to change, had built up around the concept of massed infantry. Generals fought their battles like oversized chess matches, and the unfortunate troops were dressed as conspicuously as possible, so that commanders could recognize their units at a glance. In addition, there were the requirements of firepower. Since the flintlock delivered relatively few shots per unit time, the soldiers stood side by side and several deep in order to give density to their fire and establish fire superiority. Firing was done by volleys, upon command, like a sailing ship's broadside. The soldiers leveled their pieces in the general direction of the enemy's phalanx and opened fire. While they were reloading, the enmy had *his* turn; the survivors returned fire, and so on. Coaxing rapid fire out of a flintlock could be done only by the fastest reloading. Hence, the military arm was bored out smooth, and fired a loosely fitting bullet. This bullet was of enormous caliber, operating on the excellent theory that a large erratic bullet might cause more damage than a small erratic bullet. Gas leakage between bullet and barrel allowed the use of one-ounce bullets without excessive recoil.

The barrels of these weapons were made by wrapping iron strips around a mandrel or rod, and pounding them over a forge until the edges were welded together. Afterward the outside and inside of the rough barrels were ground and reamed to passable smoothness. Often the finished product was not completely straight, much less finished to close tolerances. A musket of say, caliber .69, would take a cast lead ball about .05 inches smaller than the bore diameter. The ball rebounded from side to side as it rattled down the barrel and invariably left in some direction other than the one in which it was pointed, its final direction being determined largely by whichever side of the barrel it struck last before leaving. However, if the range was short enough, it could be relied upon to hit *someone* in a large mass of men. Shooting the musket at anything beyond point-blank range was a waste of time and lead. The target, unless about the size of a double bed sheet, enjoyed a high degree of immunity, but objects to either side, or at a greater or lesser range, were in extreme danger.

In spite of the manifest superiority of rifle over musket, the latter weapon was the mainstay of the Revolution. For the underlying reasons we must dig into the matter of supply.

The outbreak of open rebellion in 1775, found the American Colonies fighting a war almost without weapons to fight with. Though the beginning of the war had long been regarded as only a matter of time, the Colonies did little to store materiel in preparation for that which was inevitable. Weapons on hand in the arsenals were as few and diversified as the people who settled the country. They consisted chiefly of British imports and various relics of the French and Indian Wars. The frontier families, of course, owned firearms, but protecting a homestead and protracted fighting are two different things. Organized warfare, then as now, required quantity and standardization in order to facilitate replacement and supply. The frontier rifles were made to individual specifications; few were of exactly the same caliber and interchangeable parts were unknown. There were no replacement parts. If a sear spring, for instance, were to break during a campaign, the weapon had to be discarded.

But though few in number, the riflemen caused quite a splash in military circles. At first, the American rifle and rifleman was regarded by the British Military as something of a curiosity, a freak. They treated the rifle's power with contempt—and paid for it. Later, it began to seriously worry them. The sniping practices of the colonial militia were roundly damned as being cowardly, unfair, and the most absolutely unsportsmanlike innovation they ever saw. Besides, they were getting the daylights shot out of them. Officers, in particular, were killed at what were then phenomenal ranges. The rules for proper conduct of warfare made absolutely no impression on the woodsman; likely as not, he had never heard of them. As civilians, not versed in formal military tactics, the Colonials were well-adapted for improvising the best tactics for their new weapon. The rifleman had been reared on Indian fighting, and had learned to fight them on their own terms. He was as self-sufficient as a cat, never having expected anything but hardship. He came out of the forests completely equipped, carrying his long rifle, ammunition, bullet molds, and other accouterments with him, and was apparently disturbed not at all by the prospect of walking several hundred miles to the scene of action. And he left behind him a giant's legend. There are, naturally, many outlandish tales of the incredible skill of the Colonial marksman, which the writer will mercifully pass over. For extraordinary shots are just that; they in no way represent the normal effectiveness of the weapons in use. But whatever the real reason, King George III did negotiate with his German cronies to recruit German marksmen and hunters, probably on the sound tactical principle of fighting the Americans, rifle against rifle. However, these "Hessians" were armed with the old European rifle, as inefficient as its American counterpart was deadly. After being almost annihilated in the Green Mountain Battle, they figured only insignificantly in the remainder of the war. Their most noteworthy achievement was getting ambushed by Washington's commando raid across the Delaware River one Christmas Eve night.

The American riflemen seem to have appeared and disappeared like phantoms, doing wonderful work in one engagement, not appearing at all in another. The Army enlistment period was a short one. At its conclusion, the enlistees would return home, taking with them their weapons and any Colonial supplies that were not nailed down. It was this all too human practice that in 1777, led General Washington to order that all Government arms be stamped with the letters, "U.S."

The ebb and flow of the Army's strength, both in personnel and material, made it a highly unstable fighting force. The bulk of the fighting was, of necessity, done by the militia, trained to fight as the British were trained. But with the Colonial manpower and firearms problems, the British generals never knew just what was going to oppose them. Nor did the Americans, for that matter.

To meet the enormous and continuous demand for firearms, the Colonies had two choices open to them. One way was to procure them abroad. The other was to requisition and build them themselves. Committees of Safety had been formed, in the spring of 1775, throughout the colonies to exploit the latter idea. The country was scoured for available arms, and gunsmiths, or people claiming to be gunsmiths, were given contracts to manufacture smoothbore muskets. There were only a few gunsmiths capable of producing good rifles, and the manufacture of such arms took a great deal of time, so the musket was to remain the principal weapon of the Revolution. On November 4th, 1775, the Continental Congress passed a resolution recommending the several colonies to construct flintlock muskets of caliber .75, with barrels 3 ft, 8 inches in length. However, most of the Colonial Committees of Safety had already set up their own specifications, or set up none at all, as in the case of Rhode Island. Most manufacturers copied the British "Brown Bess" musket. Stocks of foreign parts were utilized wherever possible. Everybody was making weapons of different size. Rising prices and materials shortages made the arms contractor's life a bleak one. The result was a sort of regimented chaos. Such was the state of things that Benjamin Franklin, ordinarily an astute man, seriously advocated arming our troops with bows and arrows. By early spring, 1777, the American Army was as poorly armed a group as ever tackled the British Lion.

Early in 1776, Congress had sent Silas Deane to Paris to extract all possible aid from the French Government. Shortly afterwards he was joined by Benjamin Franklin and Arthur Lee. Franklin, the complete antithesis of the French courtiers, was nonetheless a great personal success. The House of Bourbon was unwilling to openly back a candidate who might lose, but to the French, the thought of weakening Britain was like the taste of wine. Accordingly, the royal arsenal at Charleville was authorized to sell thirty thousand Model 1763 muskets to various commission houses, who turned the muskets over to American representatives. In March, 1777, a ship bearing twelve thousand muskets arrived at Portsmouth, New Hampshire, and another ship, carrying eleven thousand muskets docked in Philadelphia. This windfall put the American Army back in business, ending their once dire shortage of shoulder arms. It also ended the rifle's chance of becoming the predominate weapon. Of all the various makes of French muskets that eventually saw service in the Revolution, the most important was the Model 1763 Charleville, not only from a quantity standpoint, but because it served as the pattern for the first United States shoulder arms when, after the war, Springfield and Harpers Ferry were established as our national arsenals.

The turning point of American fortune occurred in October, 1777, at the Battle of Saratoga. The British had long recognized New England as the real backbone of the rebellion. It became their determination to isolate New England from the rest of the country and await the subsequent surrender of the colonies. The logistical ball got rolling, and a large force of British, Canadian, and German troops, plus several Indian tribes, some seventy-two hundred in all, was assembled in Canada. The plan was to send this force, under the command of General Burgoyne, to the head of the Hudson River. Thereafter, they were to follow the Hudson to Albany, where they would be joined by General Clinton's forces, the other half of the scissors, who were to move northward from New York. Successful completion of this brilliantly conceived plan would have undoubtedly meant the defeat of the young nation.

However, things went sour, almost from the beginning. Burgoyne's armies reached the left bank of the Hudson River on the 30th of July, after overwhelming the American resistance in their way. But Burgoyne had made a vast strategic error in employing Indian savages as his allies. New Englanders, who were fully aware of the implications, knew better than to be overrun by Indians. Furthermore, the Indians recognized no difference between Tory and Rebel. Friends of the royalist cause were in as much danger as anyone else. The British Army managed to collect before itself a mass of opposition such as the new nation had never before produced. Recruits swarmed down from the mountains and neighboring towns. A Canadian expeditionary column sent to reinforce Burgoyne was unable to fight its way through to join him. A large force of German troops, detached from the main British body for a foraging raid, was routed, leaving its commander dead in the wilderness. By the 14th of September, Burgoyne reached Saratoga heights, about sixteen miles from his goal at Albany. The Americans, having fallen back from Saratoga stood firm and resolved to give no further.

By October, Burgoyne was in serious trouble. The Indians and Canadians were deserting; the American forces, on the other hand, were still swelling with new recruits. The British position had become untenable, so Burgoyne attacked; there was nothing else he could do. After a daylong fight, the British forces withdrew from contact, in considerably worse shape than when they started. Casualties were heavy and their deputy commander, General Frazer, had been dropped out of the saddle by some backwoods rifleman. Action dragged on for some days, but the Americans, having everything their own way, refused a decisive battle, and were content to hold the British at bay. Clinton's troops in the south were making but slow progress and on the 13th of October, starvation forced Burgoyne to surrender his entire command, some fifty-eight hundred men.

It was an unheard of victory. An entire British army had given up and surrendered, and the American cause was suddenly turned from defeat to victory. News of Burgoyne's defeat reached Paris just as the American commissioners, in despair, were about to forget the subject of French aid and were trying, unsuccessfully, to negotiate with the British. As if by magic, all difficulties with the French simply evaporated. France promptly signed a treaty acknowledging the independence of the United States. This amounted to a declaration of war with England. Spain and Holland followed hot on the heels of France. Though the numbing winter at Valley Forge, the treachery of Benedict Arnold, and the capture of Charleston still lay ahead, the achievement at Saratoga had convinced Europe and the Colonials themselves that the Revolution was just crazy enough to succeed. Largely due

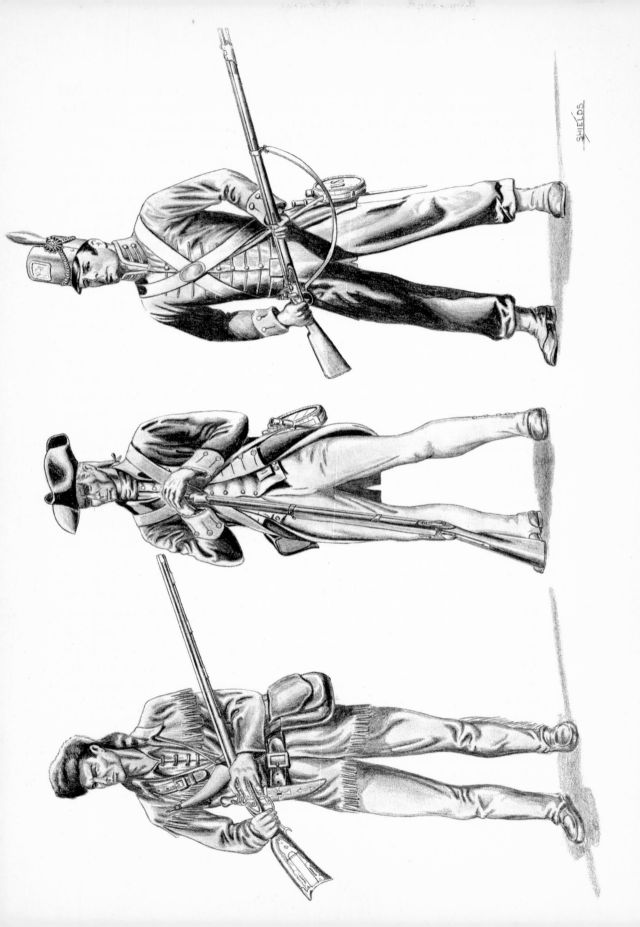

to help from the French fleet and ground forces, the Americans were able to continue fighting. Between the two, they succeeded in turning Cornwallis' refuge at Yorktown into a trap. Cornwallis surrendered on October 19, 1781. The following spring a new cabinet took over in England, which paved the way for the final peace treaty of 1783.

Committees of Safety Muskets

THE Committees of Safety Muskets, produced by the Colonies after the spring of 1775, were invariably the subject of argument among gun collectors, chiefly because they were, like the whooping crane, virtually extinct. These old flintlocks, as historically intriguing as any shoulder arms ever produced, have largely disappeared, almost without a trace.

The Committees of Safety were industrious, that much we know. Their contract muskets were made to definite specifications, copies of which exist in many state archives. A consensus of the requirements would seem to indicate a musket with a bridle lock, iron fittings, a barrel about 45 inches long, between calibers .75 and .77, held to the stock by transverse pins. There are today a fair number of muskets which may or may not have been Committee of Safety contract weapons. Yet few authenticated specimens exist. Most of the muskets are either too long, too short, or of the wrong caliber, or else vary in some latitude from the original contract specifications.

About the only way to identify one of these muskets is to consult a list of manufacturers alleged to have had contracts with some Committee of Safety. If the name of one of the makers appears on the musket, and if the musket's dimensions conform to the specifications set up by the Colony in which that manufacturer operated, the musket may be concluded to be the genuine product.

The truth of the matter is that arms which saw service in the Revolution are extremely scarce. When worn out, the replacement part problem got the better of them, and they were discarded. Later, the change from flintlock to percussion ignition saw further alteration of the surviving weapons. There also seems to be an equally good chance that the committees did not insist on rigid adherence to the specifications, so long as the product was something that would shoot.

During the race to manufacture muskets, each committee set up its own specifications, independently of, and prior to, the ineffectual Continental Congress resolution to standardize firearms manufacture.

Connecticut was the first colony to act. In April, 1775, the General Assembly passed a bill authorizing the manufacture of three thousand arms of caliber .75, with barrels 3 ft, 10 inches in length. The stocks were to have brass mountings and furniture; the lock was to be of the common type then in use, and the muskets were to be stamped with the name of the manufacturer.

Rhode Island set up no specifications whatsoever. This Colony had a sizable supply of arms which it had been collecting for years. In 1776, they supplemented their stores with private and foreign weapons, which were to be stamped with the letters CR and the Rhode Island coat of arms.

Massachusetts called for a musket to take a one ounce ball (which made it about caliber .70), a barrel 3 ft, 9 inches long, two sling swivels, and the maker's name on the lock; the whole weapon to resemble, as closely as possible, the latest British Brown Bess pattern.

New Hampshire set up no definite specifications; in fact, that Colony did not contract with manufacturers at all. Their committees attempted to procure whatever they could locate within the Colony; conditions being what they were, they might just as well have saved themselves the trouble of looking.

New York, like Massachusetts, manufactured duplicates of the latest British muskets. This was apparently the trend among all the Colonies. Pennsylvania, the home of the Colonial rifle industry, fell in line in this respect, producing muskets with 3 ft, 8-inch-barrels, 17 gauge or caliber .65, and built on the conventional British pattern.

Virginia, the only Colony to hit on the idea of centralized production, built Rappahannock Forge to take care of its arms needs. The southernmost Colonies, being less affected by the war than the northern ones, bought the bulk of their muskets from foreign dealers, who furnished them with dreadful trade muskets of the sort ordinarily supplied to African tribes.

Although, strictly speaking, the Committees of Safety muskets are not United States Government shoulder arms, they did comprise the majority of our nation's martial arms during the twenty-year-period that lapsed between their manufacture and the establishment of our first national armories.

The Flintlock Action

THE flintlock was the common weapon of the American Revolutionary War period. While made with either rifled or smoothbore barrels, the mechanism was the same in either case, and fired the powder charge by means of sparks thrown into a pan of powder by a blow of flint upon steel.

The flint, wrapped in sheet lead or leather, was clamped in the adjustable vise jaws of the hammer. The steel against which the flint struck was the rear face of the frizzen. The hammer was cocked by pulling it back against the resistance of a large V-shaped mainspring inside the lock. The frizzen, one face of which served as the pan cover, was free to pivot about the frizzen screw, and was held vertical by the frizzen spring, the V-spring on the outside of the lock plate. When the trigger was pulled, the compressed mainspring swung the hammer forward. The flint struck the frizzen a glancing blow, rotating it forward, and showered sparks into powder which lay in the pan. The priming charge exploded and flashed through a hole drilled in the side of the barrel, igniting the main charge and firing the weapon.

To load the flintlock musket, one first half-cocked the hammer and opened the pan by throwing the frizzen forward. The firer next bit off the end of a prepared paper cartridge, poured about ten grains of powder into the pan, and closed the pan by snapping back the frizzen. He then placed the musket butt on the ground, poured the remainder of the powder down the barrel, dropped a lead ball down the barrel, and wadded the cartridge paper on top of it to prevent the ball from rolling out, if the muzzle were slanted below the horizontal.

When ready to fire, he pulled the hammer back to full cock, lifted the arm to his shoulder, and pulled the trigger. The ponderous hammer swung forward, struck the frizzen and forced it open, exposing the pan to the resulting spray of sparks. The priming charge flashed through the touch hole; if all went well, the main charge let go, starting the bullet on its uncertain course.

[24]

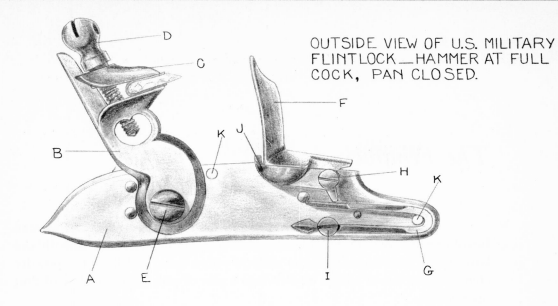

OUTSIDE VIEW OF U.S. MILITARY FLINTLOCK—HAMMER AT FULL COCK, PAN CLOSED.

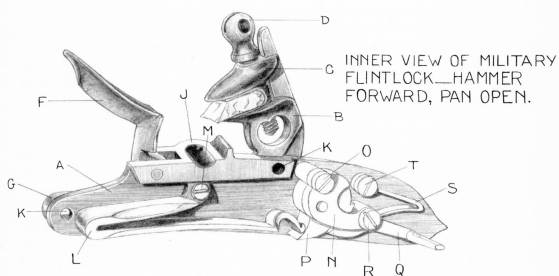

INNER VIEW OF MILITARY FLINTLOCK—HAMMER FORWARD, PAN OPEN.

A—LOCK PLATE
B—HAMMER
C—CAP
D—HAMMER SCREW
E—TUMBLER SCREW
F—FRIZZEN
G—FRIZZEN SPRING
H—FRIZZEN SCREW
I—FRIZZEN SPRING SCREW
J—PAN
K—SIDE SCREW HOLES

L—MAINSPRING
M—MAINSPRING SCREW
N—BRIDLE
O—BRIDLE SCREW
P—TUMBLER
Q— SEAR
R— SEAR SCREW
S—SEAR SPRING
T—SEAR SPRING SCREW

SHIELDS

All this took some time. There was a distinct lag between the pulling of the trigger and the ignition of the main charge. The firer had to follow through for an appreciable length of time after pressing the trigger. The jar of the hammer slamming into the frizzen was not conducive to accuracy, anyway. The military musket did not even have a rear sight, nor had it any need for one. Close aiming was useless. A brass stud on the upper band served as a sort of front sight.

The flintlock was noted for its capricious unreliability. The flint might fail to strike sparks. Powder ashes tended to clog the touch hole. Fog, rain, and snow conspired to dampen the priming charge and prevent firing.

The flintlock, with all its shortcomings, was nonetheless a great improvement over all preceding weapons. It was the best of its day, and dominated both forest and battlefield for about one-hundred-sixty years, before it gave way to the percussion system.

U. S. Flintlock Musket, Model 1795

THE years following the end of the Revolution witnessed the complete evaporation of Colonial military strength. With no war on hand, the Army fell to pieces. The Colonies, jealous of their sovereignty, feared to hand over their powers to a strong central government, and the new nation remained a loose confederation of states from 1781 until 1799. The frontiers were the scene of constant fighting, but the Indian wars did not form any immediate threat to national security, and the danger ended in 1794, when "Mad" Anthony Wayne broke the back of Indian power. The weak Federal Government made regular inventories of all existing stores of arms, but did not, or could not, make any move to replenish the stock of weapons which dwindled and shrank as the years passed.

It was not until April 2, 1794, that Congress authorized the procurement of seven thousand new muskets, and provided for the establishment of two armories for their manufacture and storage. The first of these to begin operations was Springfield armory, Massachusetts, where rudimentary facilities were already in existence. This armory, officially established in 1795, re-

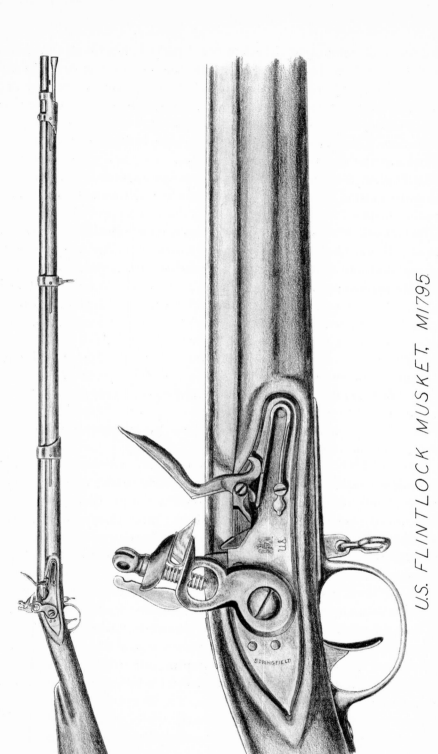

U.S. FLINTLOCK MUSKET, M1795

SHIELDS

mains one of our leading producers to this day, and many of our finest arms, including the M1 rifle, were designed and manufactured here. The second armory was located at Harpers Ferry, Virginia. Though it did not begin production until 1801, it eventually manufactured over half a million arms before it was burned, in 1861, to prevent capture.

The seven thousand firearms were patterned after the French Model 1763 Musket, the Charleville. The first of these muskets were neither marked nor dated until 1799, when the familiar spread eagle was selected as the emblem to be stamped on the lock plate of both Springfield and Harpers Ferry products.

The Model 1795 was an ordinary smoothbore flintlock, without any unusual features. It was bored to caliber .69, or about the size of a modern 16 gauge shotgun. The length was 59.5 inches, just a shade under 5 feet, and its weight averaged a little under nine pounds. The lock plate, 6.6 inches long and 1.3 inches at its widest point, was flat, with the edges filed to a bevel. The hammer, massive and strong, was also flat and bevel-edged, and had a double neck to strengthen the lower vise jaw. The upper end of the hammer terminated in an ornamental curl. The pan was made separately from the lock plate and consisted of three beveled faces which tapered together at the bottom; it had a fence at the rear to prevent the loss of priming powder. The lock plate was stamped, Springfield, in a vertical curve behind the hammer, and the eagle emblem was stamped between the hammer and the frizzen spring, surmounting the letters, U.S.

The round iron barrel was 44.75 inches long, and the earliest models were stamped with the letters VPL as proof marks. Later ones bore the familiar P, eagle's head, and V, reading from the muzzle down, after having passed through several intermediate styles of proof stamping. The barrel was held to the stock by three bands, after the French system instead of following the British practice, wherein the barrel was secured to the stock by transverse pins.

All the metal parts were made of iron, polished to a bright finish. The upper band was divided so that two rings encircled the barrel. The middle band was a single ring, from which hung the upper sling swivel. The lower band, considerably wider at the bottom than at the top, was held to the stock, as were the other two, by retaining springs set behind each band. The trigger guard was a one piece affair whose total length, including guard bow and tangs, was 13 inches.

U. S. Flintlock Musket, Model 1808

THE progressive refinement of flintlock muskets between 1795 and 1844 was of a most unspectacular sort. There were no radical changes brought about by new inventions or the stress of warfare which might demand a newer and better musket. Rather there were slow, gradual, and almost imperceptible improvements, as the manufacturers simplified production or ironed out some minor wrinkle in the flintlock's mechanism.

The Government had on hand a heterogeneous assortment of muskets, what with their store of old muskets and two arsenals which manufactured guns that differed in minor details. Then too, the reliance on private contractors resulted in muskets which all varied in some degree. To solve the problem, a new model would issue forth from the arsenals every so often, and each new model would only serve to compound the error, for it too would be put out with variations and would take its place among the already diversified group of muskets.

The first of these new models came out in 1808, after enough minor changes had been made in the Model 1795 to justify calling it a new model. The Model 1808 was remarkably like its predecessor, and at casual glance one may easily pass for the other.

The caliber, like that of the Model 1795, was .69, and the total length was 59 inches. The lock plate was about 6.5 inches by 1.25 inches at the points of greatest dimensions, and was marked between the hammer and frizzen spring with a spread eagle surmounted by the letters U.S. Below the eagle the word Springfield was stamped in a horizontal curve. The date of manufacture appeared horizontally at the rear end of the lock plate.

The lock plate was flat and bevel-edged; the rear end tapered to a prominent point. The hammer was flat and similarly finished; unlike the Model 1795, its upper end was plain. The pan was an integral part of the lock plate forging, and was semicircular in outline instead of beveled.

The stock and furniture were similar to those of the Model 1795. The stock was 56 inches long, made of black walnut, as were virtually all of our

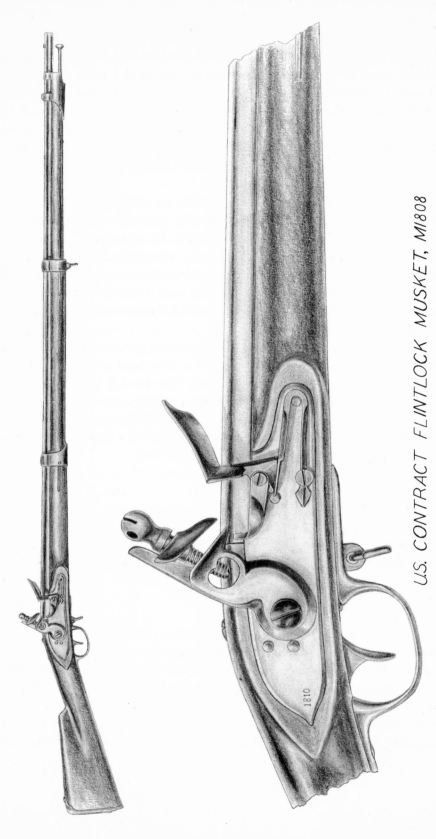

U.S. CONTRACT FLINTLOCK MUSKET, M1808

shoulder arm stock. The three bands which held the 44.5-inch iron barrel to the stock were of the pattern set forth by the Model 1795, a two-strap upper band, a middle band carrying the front sling swivel, and a rear band wider at the bottom than at the top. All three were retained to the stock by springs set to the rear of each band. The barrel was proof-marked at the breech by a P, eagle's head, and V. The trigger guard was 10 inches long, with rounded tangs, as contrasted with the 13-inch, pointed-end trigger guard of the Model 1795.

The two salient differences between the Model 1808 and the Model 1795 lay in the hammer and priming pan design. The pan of the Model 1808 was round and built as part of the lock plate and the hammer was distinguished by its lack of ornamental curling at its upper extremity. There was also a slight difference in the design of the frizzens of each weapon. The upper end of the Model 1795 frizzen was curved slightly away from the hammer, while that of the Model 1808 was plain. The other differences were largely a matter of small dimensional variations.

The Model 1808 was built during the heyday of private contracting and hand manufacturing of Government shoulder arms, and every conceivable minor variation may be expected and found. The Model 1808 used in the illustration is one of these contract arms, made in 1810. As on many of these early contract weapons, there is no name by which it can be identified. The only markings are the Government proof stampings, and the date of manufacture marked in a horizontal line behind the hammer.

U. S. Flintlock Musket, Model 1812

BY 1812, it was fully realized that production of the Model 1808 musket, as made by the Government Armories and private contractors, had not in any degree achieved the desired standardization of our small arms. The Ordnance Department took a deep breath and again plunged into cold water, this time selecting a master model and requiring both armories and all contractors to adhere strictly to the pattern and not try anything original. But the ever-present loophole was still open; each factory had

U.S. FLINTLOCK MUSKET, M1812

on hand a lot of partially finished muskets and a large stock of old parts, and these were to be used until the supply was exhausted. As it turned out, it made no practical difference; the outbreak of the War of 1812 soon afterwards forced the temporary abandonment of the standardization scheme as parts of all sorts of weapons were used in a desperate effort to supply our forces. The end of the war was to find the armories stocked with as dissimilar a group of weapons as did the end of the Revolution, making the Model 1812, from a collectors' standpoint, almost impossible to classify.

However, the design of the Model 1812 would have produced a good flintlock, as flintlocks go; but what with the war, the Model 1812 remained a sort of formless composite weapon until about 1815, when some definite recognizable pattern began to emerge from the armories. It was a standard flintlock with no really unusual features, bored to caliber .69, smoothbore, with a total length of 57 inches.

The lock plate was flat with beveled edges and measured 6.4 inches by 1.3 inches. The round-bottom pan, made integral with the lock plate, was positioned horizontally and had a fence to the rear. The double neck hammer had a curved outer surface, a ready means of distinguishing the musket from the previous Model of 1808. The lock was stamped with the word Springfield in a horizontal curve between the hammer and frizzen spring, the word being sandwiched between the letters U. S. and a spread eagle facing rearward. The date was stamped horizontally behind the hammer.

The stock was surprisingly modern in appearance, for the small of the stock did not extend into the comb, as in the two previous models. The Springfield products had a cheek recess on the left side of the stock.

All metal work was of iron, polished to a bright finish. The 42-inch round barrel was held to the stock by three bands, anchored in position by retaining springs. The upper band had two straps which circled the barrel; the middle band, 1-inch wide, held the upper sling swivel; the lower band, which measured .75 of an inch at the top by 1.75 inches at the bottom, conformed to the set pattern in its outward flare at the bottom.

The Model 1812 is easily distinguished from the Model 1808 by its round hammer and the absence of grooves running into the stock comb. The cheek recess serves to identify only the Springfield Armory musket. Collectors sometimes attempt to sub-classify this weapon by the arrangement of the band retaining springs, some having the springs to the rear of each band, some having spring actuated studs forward of each band, and a third group with plain band springs forward of each band. Generally speaking, the spring arrangements were made chronologically in the above order, but this musket was a wartime model, and the spring arrangement is an uncertain guide.

U. S. Flintlock Musket, Model 1816

DURING the period immediately following the War of 1812, the Ordnance Department seemed to be infinitely far from the goal of its thwarted attempt to provide one standard shoulder weapon for our forces to shoot; and each war only served to increase the complexities. But it was trying, anyway, and in 1815, established rigid specifications, and no nonsense this time, to be followed to the letter for the manufacture of a new service musket. In 1816, several muskets were made and established as standard, and taps, dies, and patterns were made along with them and sent to both armories (something that seems to have been neglected before) so that everyone could begin manufacture from identical prototypes.

The completed patterns were made with some departure from the Model 1812, innovations that were probably learned during the War of 1812. That part of the lock plate behind the hammer was finished in a smoothly curved surface, while the forward portion remained flat with beveled edges, establishing a style that was to last as long as we manufactured flintlock muskets. The pan, which formerly corroded badly after repeated firing, was made as a detachable unit, and of brass, rather than iron. It had no fence, but was tilted upward to the rear. The top of the frizzen was bent forward, away from the hammer, and the small of the stock was thickened and strengthened, leaving it with no comb whatsoever, another distinguishing feature of the Model 1816.

The passage of a few years' time did indeed indicate that both contract and Government arsenal weapons were being made with increasing uniformity, but this progress was due more to improved shop methods and better machinery than to the various planned efforts devoted to standardization; something called mass production was coming into its own.

This remarkable advance in manufacturing technique changed the face

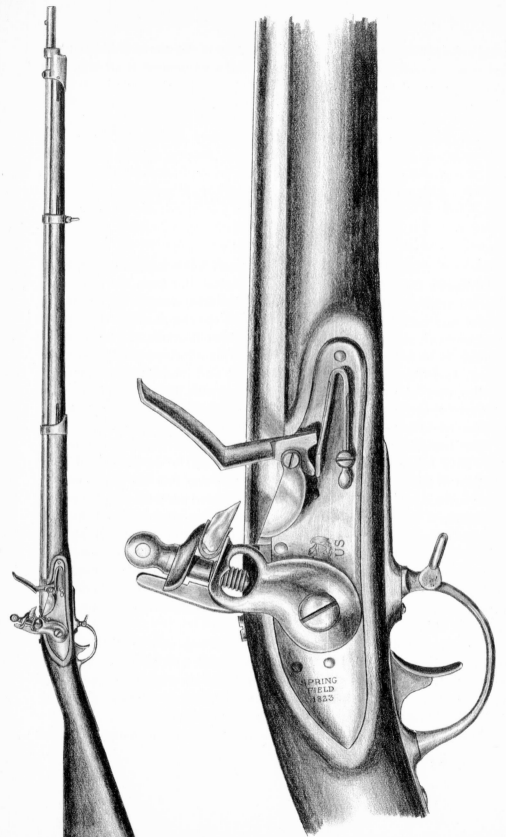

SHIELDS

U.S. FLINTLOCK MUSKET, M1816

SPRING FIELD 1823

of warfare as much as any new conception has ever done. Bear in mind the appallingly primitive gunmaking methods of the Revolutionary War period. Arms factories, as such, were unknown. Commercial weapons were made one at a time by individual gunsmiths who produced at the snappy rate of about five rifles a year. Even the great Government arsenals in Europe housed large numbers of skilled craftsmen who had at best only a rough division of labor. Each completed weapon, every forging, spring, every operation, was almost entirely the end product of the work of one man, who filed out all the parts and tediously fitted and scraped at the loose pieces until they became a working weapon. Each musket or rifle resembled its mates in a general way, but its components would interchange with those of another gun only through pure luck. And yet, within comparatively few years, American manufacturers were turning out weapons which were carbon copies of one another.

The salient figure in this industrial metamorphosis was Eli Whitney, the inventor of the cotton gin, in itself no small achievement. Back in 1798, we appeared to be drifting into another war, this time with France, and the Government was again contracting with private firms to produce firearms. In an age when such things just weren't done, Whitney proposed to manufacture muskets whose parts would actually interchange with those of any other musket he manufactured. And ridiculous as the idea seemed, he obtained a contract to manufacture ten thousand stands of muskets, to be delivered within two years. Whitney's plan for mass-producing muskets, while requiring a lot of complex power-driven machinery, was simple in the extreme—all parts were to be cut to the same dimensions of some fixed pattern and the actual assembly, heretofore a critical operation, could be done by anyone with a set of unbroken fingers, a screwdriver, and a vise. The magnitude of this achievement can be appreciated only when we realize that Whitney had to begin at zero level. He could not consult another plant in an allied business or draw on anyone's experience; nobody had any. Machine tools, such as milling machines, were yet to be invented. So Whitney, apparently considering this to be at worst a minor inconvenience, designed and built the necessary machinery himself, bucking prejudice, ignorance, ridicule, and the usual guffaws every foot of the way. The contract actually consumed eight years instead of two before it was completed, but Whitney had done that which had been nonexistent; he had succeeded in reducing an extremely complex process to a series of simple operations. Workmen with little or no experience could operate his machinery and turn out by the hundreds the various parts of a musket with so much precision that "the several parts . . . were as readily adapted to each other as if each had been made for its respective fellow."

Bit by bit, his system crept into private industry and into the Federal arsenals, and the Model 1816 was partially, at any rate, made by machine and assembly line methods.

So the Model 1816 was better made than its predecessors, though in outside appearance it differed very little from the smoothbores we had been turning out since 1795. It was a smoothbore flintlock musket, caliber .69, totaling some 57.5 inches in length. The lock plate was 6.8 inches long by 1.75 inches wide, mounting a rounded double neck hammer and a tilted brass pan, as previously mentioned, and was finished by a case hardening process which produced a mottled colored surface, similar in appearance to that of an oil film on water. It was marked between the hammer and the frizzen spring with the United States spread eagle which faced rearward, and the word Springfield and the date in three vertical lines.

The barrel, bearing the P, eagle's head, and V proof marks, was finished by browning instead of polishing. All metal furniture was similarly browned by an acid bath process, reducing the rusting that invariably happened to polished metal.

Three metal bands secured the barrel to the stock. The upper band was the standard two-strap type, and the two lower bands were also of the pattern established by previous models. Each of the lower bands was held in position by a band spring forward of the bands themselves. To simplify manufacture, the trigger guard was riveted to the trigger guard plate, a metal strip about 9.8 inches long.

About 1821, several extremely minor changes were incorporated in the musket in an attempt to insure uniformity in various contract weapons. Such muskets have sometimes been called the Model 1822; actually, there is no such animal. The Model 1816 remained the Model 1816 until it was superseded in 1835, by a new model designation.

U.S. Flintlock Musket, Model 1835

THE last smoothbore flintlock musket to be made by the United States was the Model 1835, deservedly the last, for the whole concept of flintlock ignition had long been obsolete. By this time flintlock development had gone as far as it could go. The system did not lend itself at all to multifiring arrangements, or breechloading, or accuracy, for that matter. It was almost malevolently unreliable in damp weather, and no matter how many refinements it underwent or how many new models came out, the finished product was just another flintlock embodying all the limitations inherent in the system.

So we expect little new to be found in the Model 1835, and the guess is a sound one. The model 1835 was an adaptation of the French Model 1822 Musket, the United States product, because of one delay or another, not being manufactured until 1844, the year that our first percussion musket went into production. Most of the Model 1835s were later altered to the percussion system, and are rarely found in original condition.

The musket itself was the usual caliber .69 smoothbore whose length was 57.75 inches, and weighed a little under ten pounds. The lock plate, after the fashion of the Model 1816, was flat and bevel-edged forward of the hammer and convexly rounded behind it, and was marked between hammer and frizzen spring with a spread eagle surmounting the letters U.S. and behind the hammer with the word Springfield and the date in three vertical lines. The hammer, whose surface was also round and convex, was of the standard double-necked pattern. The pan, a detachable brass unit, was mounted horizontally and had a fence to the rear.

The barrel, 42 inches long and stamped with the standard V, P, and eagle's head proof marks, was held to the stock by three polished iron bands, the upper of which was double strapped, with a brass front sight on the front strap. The other two bands were of established pattern, the uppermost mounting the front sling swivel. The lower band was, conventionally,

SPRING
FIELD
1840

SHIELDS

U.S. FLINTLOCK MUSKET, M1835

wider at the bottom than at the top; both were secured to the stock by springs forward of each band The lower sling swivel was mounted on the front of the trigger guard.

All told, the Model 1835 is quite similar to its predecessor, the Model 1816. The salient visual differences lie in the stocks (the Model 1816 has no comb and the Model 1835 stock has a big one), and the pan of the Model 1835 is horizontal with a fence, as opposed to the tilted fenceless pan of the Model 1816. Lastly, the jaw screw hole in the hammer of the Model 1835 is circular. In every other model the hole was heart-shaped.

This musket, though hopelessly dated, enjoyed continuous production by private contractors for the Government up until 1848. This was twelve years after Sam Colt's first successful revolver appeared on the market, and only a few years shy of the appearance of metallic cartridges. Our Government was manufacturing museum pieces.

Footnote to History

THE War of 1812, brought about chiefly by the British maritime practice of impressing American seamen into service with the British navy, began in a jumble of confusion that made the Revolution seem almost well-planned. The nation retained what amounted to an absolute horror of a centralized standing Army and relied on its ill-trained militia, recruited for twelve-month periods, to furnish the bulk of our fighting force. This militia occupied a unique position in military history as an armed service that never received any military training. The few days set aside each year for training were farcical and ended up without exception as weekend-drunks. The politically appointed commanders served as a claque for whichever governor was in power. No unit could be relied upon for offensive operations for when the chips were down a state might, if the war were unpopular, refuse to raise troops or having raised them, prevent them from moving out of the state borders. New England, foreseeing the ruin of its trade, refused to play, took its marbles and went home, and sat brooding all through the war, loftily disdaining to have anything to do with the fighting. The standing professional Army, what there was of it, could consider itself fortunate to hang together much less fight a campaign, and was generaled by tired old Revolutionary veterans who had never commanded large units in their lives. All the horses used to pull artillery had been sold, the Army being unable to pay the feed bill. Overall strength was about sixty-eight hundred men, and the junior-grade officers, never having received any military training either, were as ignorant on military matters as the men under them; there was no school wherein they could learn. West Point had been established, but almost hounded out of existence by regulations. And we sent this against the nation that was beating Napoleon.

On the strategic level, we began the fight with a grandiose impractical scheme for the invasion and capture of Canada. In a sense it was a good idea, and the sooner the invasion was begun, the better its chances for success. Alas, a successful military campaign requires a successful military establishment, and the young nation failed to fulfill the requirements of this simple axiom. We had cause and will and strength, but unfortunately no means with which to do it. So the war opened as might be expected with a series of absolute disasters, four expeditionary columns whose defeats furnish eloquent though usually unheeded proof of the fallacy in our concept of a million men springing to arms overnight. The first column, under General Hull, scuttled back to Detroit like a wounded crab after its first skirmish with the British, and surrendered the town to a force one third its number. The second was almost wiped out at Queenstown Heights while three thousand New York militia, to what should be their everlasting shame, watched the slaughter from across the New York border, declining to cross the state line. The commander of the beaten force resigned, to be succeeded by a political hack whose own troops, goaded beyond endurance by his comic-opera bravado and lack of enthusiasm for actual fighting, shot up his tent one night and chased him out of camp. The last expedition, a force of Kentuckians, was killed or captured to a man in its first engagement. Our western frontier, far from extending into Canada, was now under attack.

It was only the Homeric work of the tiny American Navy that kept us in business at all during the first trying years, but during the time of our naval victories, the British (who had been fighting several wars at once) managed to beat Napoleon to a standstill, freeing veteran troops for the conquest of America. By 1814, they were ready to invade our eastern seaboard and on August 18th of that year they struck and struck hard, landed in Maryland, brushed aside the terrified American militia, marched into Washington and burned it. But now, though America was theirs for the taking, British commanders inherited the same problem which had puzzled their Revolutionary ancestors. The American forces, though they often did not fight well, showed absolutely no inclination to surrender. They remained in the field, always a threat, and the British found themselves at a loss to defeat an Army which would not gather together to be defeated. The English dependence upon supplies from the sea forced them to withdraw to their ships and try again at Baltimore. This time they met intrenched riflemen and determined resistance, all protected by the bastions of Ft. McHenry. The bombardment and attack were unsuccessful and the British pulled out, losing once and for all the opportunity to retake their lost Colonies.

Meanwhile up north, the Americans whose campaigns had represented the *reductio ad absurdum* of warfare began to tighten up, and after learning about warfare the hard way, fought with ever increasing ferocity and wound up the year 1814 with battles which remain among the most bitter ever fought under our flag, securing the northern frontier against invasion.

Ultimately, it was not military victory which ended the war—it was economic necessity, war-weariness, and political trends among the American and English populace. The war was, except for the far western frontier, an unpopular one. All of New England was dead set against it, and attempts to negotiate for peace were started shortly after the war began. Nor were the British very happy. Though they had beaten Napoleon's armies and marooned the squat little Emperor on Elba, the peace efforts at Vienna weren't going at all as expected, and this uncertainty, plus demands from merchants and manufacturers to re-establish trade with *somebody,* led the Crown to accept negotiations it had spurned a few years earlier. The truth is that the war had boiled down to a sorry affair wherein each side, being denied a clean cut victory, had more to lose than to gain by continuing fighting. Lest anyone doubt it, let him remember that the peace treaty did not contain one word about the causes over which the war was originally fought. The only thing agreed to was a sort of indefinite suspension of hostilities.

The brightest victory of the war, and the big military lesson as far as weapons were concerned, was that of the Americans in the Battle of New Orleans, a battle which had no effect on the course of the war, inasmuch as it was fought after the peace treaty had been signed. The British, thwarted at last along the Canadian border, meant to split the continent by a southern invasion, and sent ten thousand Napoleonic War veterans under General Packenham in an upstream advance on the east bank of the Mississippi River. Shortly before they reached New Orleans they collided with a much smaller force of Americans commanded by Andrew Jackson, whose duty it was to defend our entire southwest territory. Jackson's men, possibly the most hodge-podge group of fighters ever assembled under one flag, were for the most part expert riflemen, and when the British found them they were intrenched and barricaded behind a canal, with their right flank anchored by the mile-wide river, their left by a swamp. It was something like getting into a fist fight with a full-grown tiger, but the British were led by a brave if chauvinistic commander. They formed their ranks and strode across the flat open field at the end of which lay the ineffective-looking barricades; they advanced in noble continental style, with elegant precision, banners flying and sunlight flashing off the long slanted line of bayonets; a brave sight, a soul-stirring sight—and a rifleman's dream. They got exactly what they were asking for, and walked smack into a galling fire which cut them as though with a scythe. The charge was stopped before it really got started, the British losing their commander and over two thousand men before they were near the American positions. The wrecked expedition pulled out of contact and sailed away, to learn that since Christmas Eve they had been at peace with America.

Perhaps the war had been too easy. It did nothing to shake our belief that an untrained civilian could grab grandpappy's squirrel rifle off the mantelpiece, leave his plow in the furrows, march off in the general direction of the enemy, and beat off an invasion. Bless him, after a fashion he *could,* but the initial cost was invariably too high, beginning always with a shocking series of defeats. Citizens remembered New Orleans and forgot Queenstown Heights and the burning of their own capital, and the years which immediately followed did nothing to dispel the conviction that the minuteman constituted an adequate defense. Ever since, our country, whose political and moral structure almost demands that an enemy be allowed to pick his time and place, has entered into each war in a state of total unpreparedness.

The period between 1815 and 1835 was about as peaceful as could be expected for a country with a thousand miles or so of open frontier. The Army, as usual, was parceled out among small isolated garrisons, fighting forgotten but incessant wars with the Indians. Its officers became quite adept at handling small units, but having no real staff problems, often proved to be failures in large scale operations. This was brought out forcibly during the Seminole uprising, the war fought by the Indian inhabitants of the Florida territory purchased from Spain. In 1835 the Seminoles massacred a small detachment of troops near Tampa, and began a bitter war that eventually involved most of the diminutive regular army. The war, which might be regarded as a burlesque of supply handling had not people died for it, dragged on until 1841, when the Army began to fight in earnest, and in a short space of time removed the Seminoles from the danger list.

The country remained at peace for four years, until events on the Mexican border involved us in a war which cost the Mexican Government its shirt. The territory west of the Sabine River, the present Texas-Louisiana border, had long been considered valueless by the Mexican Government, and when a small group of American settlers moved in, they were allowed to stay and welcomed to it, the Mexican authorities charging them infinitesimal prices for acreage and granting the settlers a seven-year immunity from all taxes. Over the years, settlers streamed in; too late, the Mexicans came to regard the influx as too much of a good thing. By 1835, there were something like twenty thousand Americans in the territory, and their rifles began to validate their claims to sovereignty more than the paper manifestos of the territory's legal owner. There was growing talk of independence, and a group of Mexican soldiers sent to collect various import duties were sent back minus money and some of their men. It was a brief small flareup, and the Texans, believing the matter was settled, returned to their farms and ranches.

Surprise. General Santa Anna, newly-proclaimed dictator of Mexico, showed up in San Antonio with three thousand troops. About one hundred and fifty Texas settlers barricaded themselves in the old Alamo mission and prepared to fight and die, if necessary. And die they did, holding out for two weeks with consummate bravery; not a single American escaped alive. Inflated by his success, Santa Anna pulled the same stunt at Goliad and outdid himself by murdering three hundred and twenty prisoners. A frontier army, hastily raised by Sam Houston, engaged Santa Anna on the banks of the San Jacinto River and wrecked the general's plans, his army, and captured the general. The Texans set up an independent republic and after nine years of cold war, during which time Mexico refused to recognize the republic, but was powerless to do anything about it, became a member of the United States. This made the border problem Army business. The better part of the Army, under General Zachary Taylor, was sent to Corpus Christi and established a temporary camp. Though a touchy situation, it hardly seemed like war; there were no frenzied preparations, no stock-piling of materiel, and Taylor's troops remained where they were for seven months, totally out of contact with the Mexican forces. After months of diplomatic bickering and arbitration, punctuated on both sides by loud screams for satisfaction of national honor, Taylor's forces moved to the east bank of the Rio Grande; eventually there was some shooting, and the fat was in the fire.

It turned out to be a hard dirty fight, complicated by the fact that the Army inherited a battlefield which extended over several thousand miles of desert, mountains, and malarial coastal plain. After about a month of border fighting, the Mexican forces were beaten, and the United States Army pushed through Camargo and then southward along the high spine of Mexican territory, the Sierra Madre Mountains, taking Monterrey without too much difficulty. Far from its supply bases, the Army seemed to be in danger of being swallowed by the territory it had conquered, and an eight-week armistice was signed with the local Mexican forces who were beaten to the point where they were happy to quit.

At this point the Mexican Government changed hands again. President Paredes had begun to see the world more and more through the bottom of a drinking glass, and amidst a great hue and cry in Mexico City, was ousted from the Presidency. Enter Santa Anna. This was old stuff to the General; he had been in and out of Mexico's political saddle time and time again. From exile in Cuba he convinced President Polk that to let him through the American blockade and enter Mexico was to end the war. Naturally, the instant he reached the capital he secured the Presidency, hastily raised an army, and in the spring of 1847, lit into the Americans at Buena Vista. The attack was whipped to a standstill and at the end of the first night the Mexican troops pulled out, leaving the field in possession of the astounded Americans, who had considered themselves beaten. Santa Anna scooped up an armful of battlefield trophies and hustled off to proclaim a great victory, leaving his men to get home as best they could.

But Santa Anna soon realized that there was no time left for political shenanigans. United States troops under General Winfield Scott had occupied Vera Cruz, Mexico's largest Atlantic seaport, and had started a march to the capital. In a move that seems strangely like the Chinese truce talks in the recent Korean War, Santa Anna secured with words what he could not take by gunfire, a three-month truce talk session which he employed to fortify Mexico City. The talks failed, of course, and the United States forces renewed their advance, reached the city, and began a systematic attack on it. When things began to go too badly, Santa Anna asked for another truce to discuss peace terms. He got it and re-established his battered defensive positions. When they were rebuilt he declared the terms impossible and the

[45]

fight began again, this time ending in the storming of Chapultepec fortress and total victory for the Americans.

The war was over. The United States demanded and got Texas, New Mexico, Arizona, and California. Santa Anna fled into exile again, his long career over at last. The consequences of the war were enormous; it had extended the United States clear to the Pacific Ocean and relieved Mexico of almost one half its territory. It had proved a valuable testing ground for a group of young West Point lieutenants and captains, who were to become the generals of the Civil War. They learned to solve the colossal problems of feeding and supplying troops who were scattered over immense distances; they learned infantry fighting under an exponent of offensive warfare, General Scott; they learned the importance of artillery support; in short, they became splendid, hell-for-leather fighters. What they couldn't foresee was that between their war and the next, firearms would undergo complete metamorphosis and change tactics right out from under them.

The Rifle Comes of Age

THE deadliness of rifled arms as compared with smoothbores was from the first too apparent to be denied, but for years, and with some justification, the rifle played second fiddle to the smoothbore musket. For one thing, it was not tactically suited to the requirements of the massed close-in fighting which was then in vogue. Though at first the limitations of the smoothbore had dictated the tactics to which it was suited, the tail soon came to wag the dog, and established military doctrine, by confusing cause with effect, supposed the smoothbore to be necessary in the first place. In fairness to the smoothbore adherents, the rifle *was* slow to reload, and grew progressively more so as powder residue caked the bore after sustained firing; it was difficult, expensive, and time-consuming to manufacture good rifle barrels; and the correct employment of the rifle was an almost unknown factor among military men trained in the traditional way of doing things. The smoothbore, by comparison, was cheap, easy to manufacture, easy to load, and every general and officer knew how to employ it. In fact, it was admirably suited to the warfare of the times, with this single but devastating exception—it could not be relied upon to hit anything beyond rock-throwing range.

The rifle could shoot rings around the smoothbore, so much so that rifle enthusiasts invariably gave the rifle advance billing which it could never quite live up to. Far be it from me to accuse General Washington of deliberately lying, after so many stories to the contrary, but the general once claimed that certain of our flintlock military rifles could place the majority of their shots into a sheet of stationery at 80 rods—a distance of a quarter of a mile. Really, now. Oh, well, I suppose one's favorite stories *will* improve and mellow with age, like vintage wine or cognac. The true accuracy of the rifle obviously lay somewhere between the amazing inefficiency of the smoothbore and the enthusiastic lies told about the rifle.

But just how good was the rifle? What could it actually do? First of all, its efficiency was as much due to the shooter as to the inherent accuracy of the rifle itself. The early American muzzle-loading rifles, the Pennsylvania or Kentucky types, were essentially one-man weapons. Their sighting equipment consisted of a front blade and a V-notch in a small vertical plate affixed to the barrel near the breech end. The sights were fixed; they could not be adjusted in any way. Furthermore, their combination of low muzzle velocities and spherical bullets permitted the bullets to make a comparatively large vertical drop for any range over which the rifle was fired. Every compensation taken for cross winds or varying ranges was the result of an educated guess. To this day, the process of pointing the muzzle towards some point other than the target and letting existing conditions of wind, air resistance, and gravity drive the bullet into the target is called "Kentucky windage." The more often a man fired his rifle the better he came to know it, and naturally, some people were better than others at this tricky, God-given knack. The problem might run something like this; a wilderness hunter, one experienced with his rifle's performance, sees a target at a range he estimates to be 150 yards. From the onset, his range estimation will be influenced by existing lighting conditions and the terrain over which he looks; it is his first guess. From previous firing he knows that the bullet will drop, let us say 3 feet by the time it traverses that distance; he must then aim an estimated distance over the target at a range he hopes is 150 yards. A usual and added complication is the presence of a cross wind which will drive the bullet sideways in flight and will either tend to cancel out or reinforce the normal drift of the bullet, that is, its lateral movement in the direction of the twist of the rifling. All these variables and indeterminates must be taken into account with each shot of the flintlock muzzle-loading rifle. The man behind the gun was and is as important as the built-in accuracy of the rifle itself, and the average eighteenth-century recruit, trained with abysmal ineffectiveness, was totally incapable of coaxing out of a rifle the same performance as a rifleman trained in the hard school of the frontier.

In the hands of its owner, the rifle was an extremely capable weapon. Frontier shooting contests were often built around a live and unfortunate target such as a turkey tethered behind a log so that only his head would appear. If the rifles were fired from a rest, the range was in the neighborhood of 20 rods, or 110 yards, and whoever hit that bobbing head was doing nice shooting, by anyone's standards. Of course, a turkey head can be a lot of places where the bullet isn't, and we have no way of knowing how many rounds were expended before the target suffered a direct hit.

Today, throughout the country, muzzle-loading flintlock rifles are fired in match competition against other flintlocks and the results give us a fair insight into the true accuracy of the old charcoal burners. At 200 yards it is entirely normal for experts to completely miss the ten ring, a circle 12 inches in diameter. At half that range a man may, with some rarity, put five shots out of five into the same circle, and at 50 yards possible scores occur often enough to cause no excitement. A modern rifle, by comparison, can blow the center out of that 200-yard target and do it all day long.

Actually, there is nothing inherently inaccurate about a rifled barrel which is loaded from the muzzle end. Given an accurately cast bullet, unhurried loading, sensitively weighed powder charges, and the time for cleaning the barrel between shots, the muzzle loading rifle can produce shot groups which modern rifles cannot substantially surpass. The target rifles of the 1880's proved this. The trouble lay with the means of igniting the powder charge and the conditions under which the rifle was used. The slow ignition of the flintlock and the crash of the hammer against the frizzen never helped accuracy one bit. Nor did powder-fouled barrels, deformed bullets, or variable powder charges. The hunting or military flintlock rifles never could, under service conditions, perform up to their maximum potentials.

There are nonetheless many muzzle-loading rifles capable of phenomenal accuracy. These are of the special bench rest variety, enormous affairs fitted with false muzzles to permit loading without bullet deformation; they may weigh in at around thirty pounds and are fired from the top of a heavy shooting bench, the stock resting on a couple of sandbags. They are the old-time counterparts of the modern bench rest rifle, which looks like somebody's idea of a joke, a species of field artillery, with its colossal heavy barrel and stock, its twenty-power telescopic sight, and hand-loaded ammunition. However, the conditions which make these rifles accurate are the conditions which rule them out as combat weapons. Neither the old nor the new bench rest rifles are any closer to the average military rifle than the stock model automobile is to the hot-rod racer, and as such their performances cannot be considered in evaluating those of the mass-produced items with which soldiers are armed.

So that's the story. Considering the limitations of the weapon, some remarkable shooting was done with it. At ranges in excess of 100 yards it could shoot a man to pieces without a great deal of trouble, which is more than one can say for the smoothbore. But the appropriate and sufficient reaction upon reading about the exploits of a James Fennimore Cooper hero is to yawn loudly and concentrate on the story's literary merit. Either eyesight, rifles, and luck were better in Hawkeye's time than they are today, which is unlikely, or else Cooper fell victim to his own fiction.

The Revolution had been primarily a smoothbore shooting match, due to tactical requirements, domestic manufacturing difficulties, and the fact that France shipped us tons of smoothbore muskets. But when the rifle was properly employed against the smoothbore, what followed was not so much a battle as an execution. Some of our military leaders never quite lost sight of that fact.

The rifle's cardinal limitation lay in its slow loading, something which stumped the mind of every inventor for a number of centuries. The only really adequate solution was breech-loading, but no one could design a suitable gas seal for the closed breech, there being a distressing tendency on the part of pressurized gas to come boiling out of any crack or opening. The early breech-loaders were as unkind to the user as to the target, fired at low velocities because of gas leakage, and with few exceptions seldom went past the experimental stage. Since the attempts at breech-loading were failures, the rifle remained a muzzle-loader, and designers were forced to concentrate on alleviating the rifle's loading difficulties. In the United States, the universal solution was the use of the greased patch system. In Europe, loading methods underwent dozens of changes, ultimately culminating in a system which appeared in the United States just prior to the Civil War.

The eighteenth and nineteenth century Frenchmen were demon gun designers, and until they ran out of inventive steam about the time of World War I, evolved many ideas which were eventually snapped up by other nations. In 1826, Captain Delvigne, a French infantry officer, designed a rifle barrel whose inside diameter narrowed abruptly near the breech. A spherical ball, dropped down the bore, would come to rest against this circular shoulder and was forced to expand into the rifling by repeated blows of the ramrod. The Delvigne rifle, adopted by the French Army in 1838, was improved by Captain Thouvenin, who produced a rifle known as *Le Fusil à Tige,* or stem gun. The two rifles employed only slightly different means to achieve the same result. The Thouvenin rifle barrel had a cylindrical stem screwed into the center of its breech end. The undersized ball slid freely down the barrel until it hit the projecting stem, engaging the rifling after being struck by the ramrod. In 1846 it superseded Delvigne's rifle as the standard French service rifle. No good. Both the loading methods inflicted a lot of deformation on the bullets in order to upset them into the rifling grooves, and an irregular object does not follow a regular trajectory. The rifle was regressing back to the level of the old German Jäger rifles. The bullets were warped, misshapen, and hence inaccurate, and the constricted barrels were difficult to clean, to say the least. But around 1850, another army officer of the military school at Vincennes, Captain Minié, struck inventive pay dirt when he designed a cylindrical pointed bullet whose base was deeply hollowed out. A wooden wedge or plug, inserted into the hollow base, was driven violently into the cavity by the force of the explosion, expanding the sides into engagement with the rifling. The result was not total satisfaction, because the hollow bullet was large without being dense, always a poor arrangement when the idea was to buck air resistance. But it worked; it loaded like a smoothbore and fired like a rifle, and was accurate enough to put the rifle on its own on the battlefield.

Shortly afterwards, the United States Army, experimenting with the Minié bullet at Harpers Ferry Arsenal, discovered that the wedge wasn't necessary at all. The jolt of the exploding powder charge was, by itself, sufficient to enlarge the bullet. As a side comment on the idea, we notice today that the original Minié principle is in wide use in the United States Army, in the projectile of the rifled 4.2-inch-rifled mortar. This weapon, known as a chemical mortar because it was originally designed to fire war gases and smoke, is a muzzle-loader, and the base of its twenty-five pound projectile is girdled by a brass rotating disc, whose outside diameter is about equal to that of the shell case. A steel pressure plate fits partially into the disc, and forces the brass disc into engagement with the rifling under the impress of burning propellant gases.

At any rate, the Army adopted the Minié rifle in 1855, selecting a caliber .58 bullet, and reboring existing shoulder arms to take the new bullet. The

Minié bullet and the metallic cartridge appeared in the United States almost simultaneously, and the fastest and most practical of the muzzle-loading gadgets was made obsolete as soon as it was adopted, although the two developments were used side by side all during the Civil War.

Our nation's first consignment of rifles was purchased in 1792, after President Washington, who probably had a better overall grasp of military requirements than any man in the country, decided to arm and equip a rifle battalion of about three hundred and twenty-five men. During the Revolution, Washington had relied mainly on the solid phalanx of musket-armed troops to provide the bulk of his army's firepower, but he had witnessed the rifle in action and knew a good thing when he saw it. The contract was let out to a group of Lancaster County, Pennsylvania gunsmiths, each of whom was an excellent craftsman, who worked individually and had his own ideas about the appearance and size of a rifle. Of course, none of the rifles even resembled one another closely in such particulars as caliber, barrel length, and fittings, a state of affairs which just doesn't work in a military organization. Supply troubles again. The Government made no further venture into the rifle-making field until 1803.

U.S. Flintlock Rifle, Models 1803 and 1814

AT the very beginning of the nineteenth century, someone pried out of Congress a bill authorizing the establishment of a volunteer rifle regiment; and Henry Dearborn, the Secretary of War, gave Harpers Ferry, our new arsenal, the job of manufacturing several thousand flintlock rifles to arm the proposed unit. One regiment is not an especially large body of troops, but when considered in relation to the total size of our minute Army, it was not an inconsiderable percentage figure. The production of these rifles was the first major job allocated to Harpers Ferry, and our military rifle manufacturing was thereafter centered there, Springfield doing the bulk of musket production until rifles became our standard shoulder arms. The pattern chosen as a guide to manufacture was the Pennsylvania rifle, the wise and logical choice. Though most of our muskets were pretty faithful

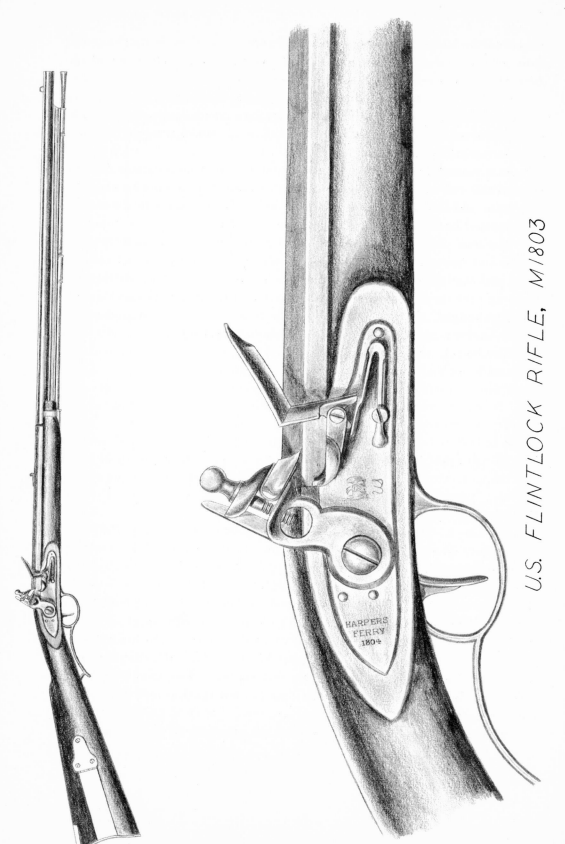

SHIELDS

U.S. FLINTLOCK RIFLE, M1803

HARPERS
FERRY
1804

copies of the latest French muskets (the European nations at that time did little rifle designing worthy of the name), we could choose from any of the best rifles in the world, the privately owned hunting arms.

Harpers Ferry was a new arsenal, and its workers must have been very individualistic men, for they produced rifles with an astounding variation in minor dimensions, so that the measurements of one rifle just might or might not correspond with those of another.

In a general way, though, the Model 1803 rifles were caliber .54, the normal rifle caliber, firing a half ounce spherical ball propelled by seventy-five grains of black powder, the ball itself being roughly one-half the weight of that used in the smoothbore musket.

The lock plate, 5.25 inches long by 1 inch wide, was flat with beveled edges, and was stamped between the hammer and frizzen spring with an eagle and the letters U.S., and behind the hammer with the words Harpers Ferry and the date. The hammer was like that of the contemporary musket, flat, bevel-edged, and double-necked. The fenced pan was rounded at the bottom and was an integral part of the lock plate forging.

The barrel, whose actual length varied from rifle to rifle, averaged out at about 33 inches; at the breech it was octagonal in cross section, becoming progressively more rounded until at the muzzle it was circular in cross section. It bore a simple open rear sight near the breech, a front blade at the muzzle, and an underside longitudinal rib, to which were affixed two small pieces of hollow tubing which served as ramrod sockets. The barrel and rib were held to the stock by one transverse sliding key. A few of these rifles were supposed to have been bored out smooth, like a shotgun, giving rise to the term "smooth rifle," a total contradiction of terms, if nothing else. Mull *that* one over some winter evening.

The stock was of the sort common to sporters more than to military rifles, being 26 inches long, about half length. It was fitted with a deep crescent-shaped butt plate, a large brass patch box on the right side of the butt, and a brass trigger guard and skeleton pistol grip.

The Model 1803 rifle was manufactured without change until 1814, when the mushrooming wartime Army called for the arming of several additional rifle regiments. The new product had a barrel 3 inches longer than that of the Model 1803, but aside from that, the Models 1803 and 1814 are almost incapable of being distinguished from one another. The Model 1814 was marked with Harpers Ferry and the date behind the hammer and with a spread eagle in front of the hammer.

The original records concerning the manufacture of these rifles were destroyed in the burning of Harpers Ferry Arsenal, and little is actually known about the number produced by the Government. However, since the nation relied almost exclusively on privately owned rifles in the War of 1812, it may safely be assumed that production was extremely limited.

U.S. Flintlock Rifle, Model 1817

MILITARY rifles take a constant beating to which sporting or hunting arms are seldom subjected. The flintlock rifle in military service needed a full length stock to protect the iron barrel, or at least a stock which was securely fastened to the barrel. The Models 1803 and 1814 had neither, and their method of securing the stock to the barrel, one transverse sliding key or wedge, proved unsatisfactory. As a remedial step, Harpers Ferry, in 1817, began construction of pilot models of what was to be the last of our muzzle-loading flintlock rifles, a type known as the common rifle. Although the patterns were Government-made, the actual manufacture, as far as is definitely known, was all done by private contractors, and Harpers Ferry continued to turn out the Model 1814 rifle, probably to make use of whatever stocks of parts were lying around the arsenal. The makers' names and other identifying markings will vary from rifle to rifle, due to the manufacturers' individual procedures, but otherwise, the Model 1817 contract rifles were all the same. The contracts were filled by Simeon North, Nathan Starr, and R. & J. D. Johnson, all of whom had plants at Middletown, Connecticut, and by Henry Deringer of Philadelphia.

The Model 1817 rifle was designed without a trace of resemblance to the Pennsylvania rifle of which it was a lineal descendant, but instead was practically a dead-ringer for the Model 1816 musket, except for barrel and stock length, caliber, and of course, the all important matter of rifling. It was bored to caliber .54, and was about 7 inches shorter than the musket, measuring 51.25 inches from the muzzle to the heel of the butt.

The lock was, except for overall size, the same as that of the Model 1816 musket, with a combination flat and convex lock plate, a rounded double necked hammer, and a detachable tilted brass pan. It measured 5.5

inches long by 1.2 inches wide, and was finished by mottled grey-colored case hardening.

The full length stock, with an oval iron-patch box on the right side of the butt, was held to the barrel by three acid-browned iron bands, each of which was the pattern used in the musket; a two-strap upper band, a middle band which held the upper sling swivel, and a lower band which was widely flared at the bottom.

The barrel was circular in cross section, exactly 3 feet long, rifled with seven grooves and was finished by acid browning. The sights were about the same as those on the Models 1803 and 1814, a rigid, non-adjustable rear notch and a front blade sight.

U.S. Flintlock Rifle, Model 1819 (Hall)

THOUGH American Ordnance has often passed up some good bets, it did beat every nation in the world to the large scale production of a breech-loading rifle, though we were not the first to use them. During the American Revolution, the Ferguson rifle, a flintlock breech-loader, had been used in limited quantity and with some success by the British at the battle of King's Mountain, but the rifle later died a natural death as the result of its excessive gas leakage at the breech and undoubtedly from the horror it caused in the minds of the conservative British Military.

In 1811, John H. Hall, an American Army captain, was granted a patent for a remarkable breech-loading flintlock rifle. A natural market for any firearm lies in its acceptance and purchase by the Military Service, and Hall tried long and hard to have his rifle tested for troop use. In 1813 he succeeded; the Army bought a few rifles and began its trials. Such things always take years, even under the impress of war, and it was not until 1817 that the Army bought one hundred rifles in order to see what a tactical unit thought of them. The reports were favorable enough and the necessary tooling-up began for the manufacture of one thousand Hall rifles, Hall himself supervising the production.

The Hall design was as simple as it was unusual. In effect, a section of

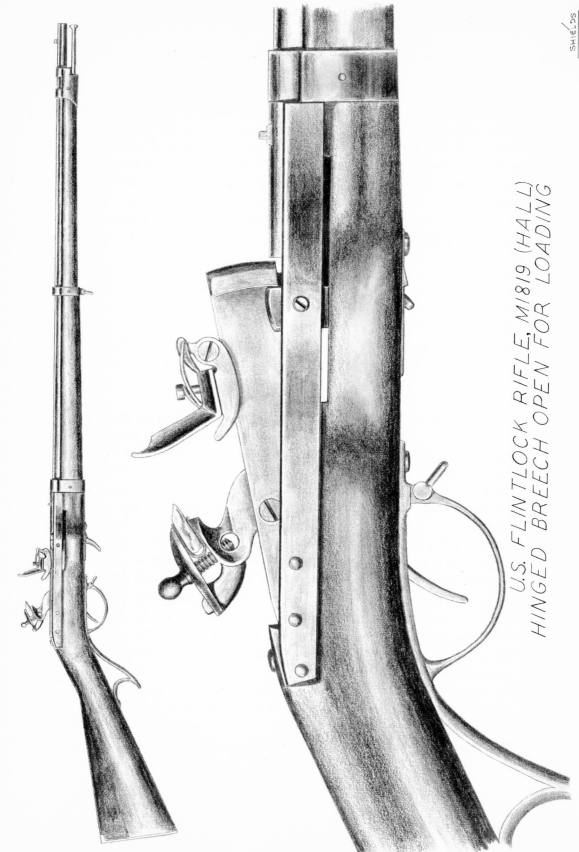

U.S. FLINTLOCK RIFLE, M1819 (HALL)
HINGED BREECH OPEN FOR LOADING

SHIELDS

the breech end of the barrel was hinged at the rear, so that it could be tilted up to expose the chamber, that part of the barrel into which powder and ball were normally placed. When tilted forward and closed, the hinged barrel section, actually a centrally bored, heavy rectangular block of metal, was in alignment with the bore of the rifle.

To load the Hall rifle, the shooter released a spring catch in front of the trigger guard, swung the hinged section upward, dropped the powder charge and the ball into the exposed chamber in the section, and pushed it back into firing position against the rear of the barrel. The mechanism used to ignite the charge was a standard flintlock hammer, frizzen, and pan mounted on the hinged block, and was primed and cocked in the same manner as the regulation rifle or musket of the day.

The Hall rifle was a fast loader, and all things considered, it functioned beautifully. But it shared the disadvantage of every other pre-metallic cartridge breech-loader in that firing was invariably accompanied by an enormous flash back and discharge of burning gas where the hinged section rested against the breech end of the barrel. The firer was not likely to be hurt, because most of the gas blew straight up; nevertheless, this singular event apparently removed enough eyebrows and caused enough nervousness to nullify its advantages, and though the rifle was made for over twenty-five years, it was never the howling success that breech-loading should have been.

Hall, in addition to his other talents, was a natural-born gadget lover. His rifle is studded with small innovations that took years to come into general use, just as happens when some modern designer thinks he's come up with a new idea. Among them was a built-in device whereby the spring tension on the trigger of every Hall rifle could be easily regulated to suit each shooter's individual preference, by the turn of a screw, an idea which lay dormant as far as single trigger rifles were concerned, until the advent of the modern target rifle. Another idea was a rod bayonet which slid back into the stock when not in its fixed position. It cropped up again in the Model 1901 Springfield rifle, but it never took hold, the detachable bayonet being infinitely superior as a utility tool and can opener to one permanently attached to the rifle. One of Hall's main contributions to gun-making was his belief in, and utilization of, the manufacturing system begun by Eli Whitney and followed by Simeon North, America's first official pistol-maker. Whitney's manufacturing procedures had led the Government to adopt power-driven drop hammers and barrel-making machinery. Though production of the Model 1816 musket was partially done with precision machinery, it remained for Hall to set up the production line of a Government arsenal so that every product was made with complete interchangeability of parts.

The Hall rifle was a caliber .52 breech-loading rifle, 53 inches long and weighing about ten pounds. The lock mechanism was set slightly off center into the hinged section or breech block, which was stamped with Hall's name, the letters U.S., and the date of manufacture. The entire breech mechanism was case hardened in a mottled grey finish.

The barrel, rifled with sixteen grooves, looked like a smoothbore when viewed from the muzzle end. The barrel was reamed out smooth at the muzzle end for about 1.5 inches, possibly to permit easy muzzle-loading, should it ever be necessary. It was coated with an extremely tough and durable brown lacquer, instead of polishing or browning, and had open sights much like those of the commercial Kentucky rifle, except that they were offset to the left to permit sighting past the hammer and frizzen.

The barrel bands, also finished with lacquer, were of standard type, except for the lower one, which had no bottom flare. The trigger guard was rather elaborate and formed a skeleton pistol grip.

Production of smoothbore muskets far outstripped that of the rifle, and in no sense did we ever use a rifle to the exclusion or even subordination of the musket. The smoothbore musket was our main-line service weapon and remained that way for years. But the Halls stayed around for a long time and saw combat service in the Seminole, Mexican, and even the Civil War. This unique rifle, while never quite doing what it should, seemed to be too nice an idea to discard entirely, and many specimens were later altered to, or manufactured for, use with the percussion system.

The Rise of Percussion Ignition

THOUGH the flintlock was in its heyday, considered to be the last word in firearms, the passage of time was to prove otherwise, and in the latter part of the eighteenth century there transpired what seemed to be an almost unrelated series of events, whose first concrete result was the total abolition of flint and steel ignition. The first step along the trail was taken by the noted French chemist, Claude Louis Berthollet, the discoverer of fulminate of silver. As the century drew to a close France was gripped by a revolution which terminated in the execution of the French Emperor, Louis XVI. Trouble was cooking on the European fire; only ten days later France declared war against England, Holland, and Spain, and the newly-formed Republic was forced to take stock of a situation which had existed for some years; a powerful and hostile sea power could at will seriously hamper the manufacture of black powder by choking off French imports of nitrates. In those days, saltpeter, the backbone of the explosives industry, was available by either of two methods. The first and easiest was by mining, but that was dependent upon the presence of large natural deposits of potassium nitrate. Failing that, saltpeter had to be made by mixing organic refuse with water and lime, leaching the decomposed mass with water, and allowing the potassium nitrate to crystallize out of solution. It was a slow, inefficient, and expensive process.

So Berthollet was placed at the head of a commission entrusted with the development of potassium nitrate in French territory, and under governmental direction, began to grope around for compounds to replace the scarce and critical saltpeter. Unfortunately for his immediate purpose, he attempted to use mixtures containing potassium chlorate or various fulminates as propellants. The latter of these compounds, especially, were sufficiently tricky to shatter the entire laboratory while being processed, and when detonated did so with enough rapidity to demolish the weapons in which they were used. Since near-instantaneous explosives were no more suitable as propellants in Berthollet's time than they are today, Berthollet abandoned his search (a fulminate of silver explosion had injured him in 1788, so he probably wasn't too put out). But though failing to produce a black powder substitute, he did prove this—that chlorates and fulminates would go off with one whale of a bang, and he must have had a lot of wrecked muskets to prove it.

A little later in 1799, Howard, an Englishman, went Berthollet one better. Back then, when a good experimental method of testing an explosive was to set fire to a batch of it or swat it with a mallet, it must have been dangerous work, but Howard confirmed what Berthollet may have already known. He took mercury fulminate, a viciously unstable compound formed by dissolving mercury in nitric acid and adding alcohol to it, managed to roll some of it into pellets without losing a thumb, and detonated it with a blow by a metal hammer.

The stage was now set, but all this high-explosive wizardry might have been forgotten or even evaded by less adventurous souls, had not someone swung the invention away from the tangent it was following. Berthollet had been using the right explosive for the wrong purpose. Any sort of metal fulminate was useless as a propellant. It was however a splendid primer—a small charge used to set off a larger one. The Rev. Alexander John Forsyth, a Presbyterian Minister in Belhelvie, Scotland, tackled the problem from this angle and the result was on par with the discovery of gunpowder. On Oct. 11, 1807, he patented his device for the "Application of the detonation principle to exploding gunpowder firearms." Forsyth's application, which opened up a new universe in firearms development, is the system in standard use today, though in greatly altered form.

The Forsyth gun lock, in essence, employed a hollow metal nipple inserted into the breech end of the barrel. The upper end of the nipple was enlarged to receive a small bit of mercury fulminate, each charge of which was measured out and fed into the nipple by an ingenious though delicate magazine. When struck by a metal hammer and a firing pin, the fulminate exploded, flashed through the vent in the hollow nipple, and fired the main charge, a conventional load of black powder and ball. The clumsy flintlock hammer, with its vise jaws and loose flint, the frizzen, and flashpan and all their attendant difficulties were eliminated at one stroke. The French Emperor Napoleon, always a fast boy in nosing out a military advantage, is reported to have offered Forsyth the sum of twenty thousand pounds sterling for his invention, and was turned down flat.

The original Forsyth lock was subsequently altered into a pill lock, in which the primers were in the form of individual pellets or pills, which were placed by hand into the nipple. None of the variations really eliminated the lock's one bad feature—a loose wad of sensitive explosive which had to be handled and placed on top of the nipple.

It remained for Joshua Shaw, a man variously described as an English artist and an American sea captain, to bring the idea to complete fruition. Perfection of an idea is usually attained when the idea is simplified down to its essence, not by complicating it, and Shaw's work eliminated the necessity for magazine-fed locks, weak and costly lock parts, and loose explosives, for it was Shaw who designed the percussion cap. His original caps were made of iron, as reloadable primers, but shortly afterwards he built them as small pewter cylinders with one closed end which held the priming mixture, sealed in by a metal foil lining. The open end was placed over the nipple, gripping it tightly and weather-proofing the gun lock. Yet the cap was an experimental failure because the pewter cap tended to melt under the heat of the explosion and dripped molten metal down the nipple, blocking it for any succeeding shot. However, Shaw had two years to think it over while sitting out some patent difficulties (he had to reside state side for two years before his idea was patentable) and during this time he designed a cap housing made of copper, the metal which has had such ubiquitous use in the firearms industry. The final product was well enough conceived to remain in use for a good half century, and cap and ball weapons were the workhorses of the American Civil War.

The Shaw percussion cap appeared in 1816, a manifest undeniable advance over the flintlock, and yet it wasn't adopted by our military forces until 1842—a gap of over a quarter century. During the time when the Prussians were using the needle gun, a primitive but workable bolt action rifle, we placed our reliance on flintlock muskets! Since this lag, this anachronism is something we notice almost every time a new weapon or improvement appears, it might be well to delve into the subject now. It is all too easy to dump the responsibility squarely into the lap of the Ordnance Department and accuse all military men of being blind to the most obvious change, a group of ivory tower inhabitants who judge the future only in terms of the past. Since this has often been completely true, the blame is usually left there without looking further. Actually, there are many other ramifications. Though it may, in this day of multi-billion dollar wars, seem ridiculous to bring the subject up at all, there is the matter of expense. A nation with tremendous stocks of usable weapons on hand will often hesitate to convert, because its present weapons, though obsolescent, at least work. And in this country civilians have a strangle hold on the military purse strings, for excellent reasons. Getting large military appropriations out of Congress in the early 1800's must have been dreadfully difficult. The nation that a short time before had abolished its entire military establishment and had just finished a costly war was not yet in the mood to vote large sums for defense. After all, we had won, hadn't we? Why change?

In addition, infant inventions are invariably imperfect inventions; the first television wasn't too hot either. And the first percussion caps were undoubtedly erratically loaded and made from materials of variable quality. When troops who were resigned to singed eyebrows, misfires, and other flintlock hazards distrusted the percussion guns, there must have been a reason. At least, that's my guess.

Then too there is the block caused by conservatism, the most valid of the criticisms leveled against our military for we tend to ridicule and underestimate that which we cannot understand. One can easily see the logical flaw in the judgment of those who opposed firearms on the grounds that they would place fighting power in the hands of cowards, for it is always easy to come to a correct solution when we are not concerned with the practical consequences of it. Or by going further back into the past, we can picture and laugh at the twelfth century knights who fingered their great broadswords uneasily and muttered prayers as they passed a wooden engine designed for throwing large rocks. Silly? One only wishes it were—when George Custer's command was wiped out at the Little Big Horn, it had left behind in camp several Gatling guns, mechanically operated machine guns. British military officers fought with tooth and nail the adoption of an armored vehicle with self-laying tracks, the tank; though it almost broke the western front stalemate shortly after it appeared in the lines. Though the military aircraft, shortly after World War I, proved itself capable of sinking battleships, it was not seriously considered as a major factor in warfare until after the Germans gave Rotterdam the world's first awful lesson in pattern bombing, and after the Japanese had smashed our Pacific fleet at Pearl Harbor. The corridors of history are lined with monuments to man's inability to grasp a new idea. And there is something of this vestigial fear in all of us—this reluctance to accept a new idea, because it is new. The old familiar arms are the best understood and the easiest to employ correctly, and only with the greatest difficulty can we realize that the very production of a new weapon is the key to its obsolescence.

At any rate, sportsmen and hunters were happily converting their flintlocks to the percussion system, and the Government arsenals continued to turn out flintlock muskets.

U.S. Percussion Musket, Model 1842

THE percussion musket, Model 1842, falls into an odd category, chiefly because it was our first regulation percussion shoulder weapon and also our last smoothbore shoulder weapon. Harpers Ferry had, in 1841, produced pilot models for a rifle equipped to use the percussion cap, and the Model 1842 was left as neither quite fish nor fowl, a hybrid arm combining

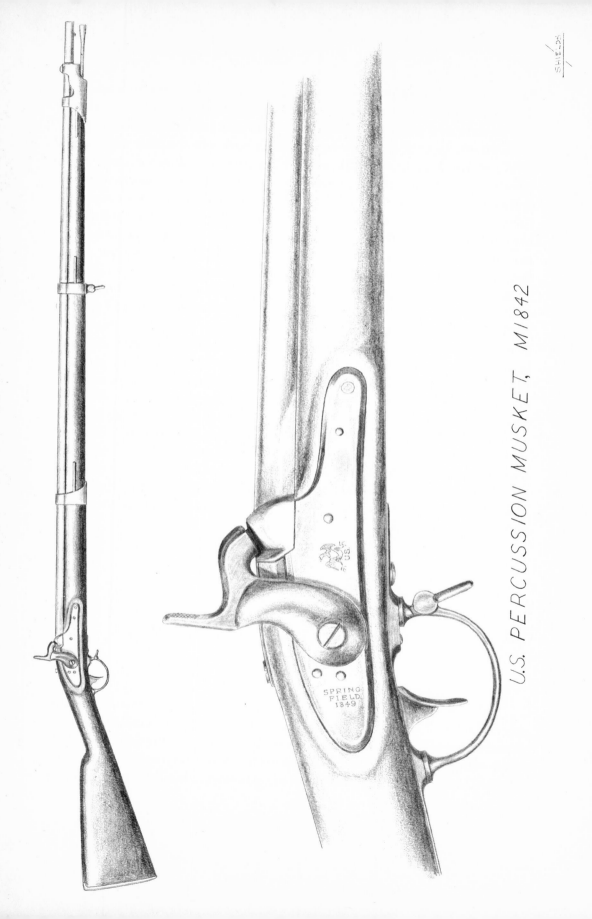

U.S. PERCUSSION MUSKET, M1842

SPRING
FIELD
1849

the new and vastly superior percussion lock and the smoothbore barrel, the relic of a system long since slated to go. It was our standard infantry weapon, however, rifle or no rifle. The Army was at that time firmly wedded to the musket, and the Model 1842 saw continuous production from 1844 until 1855, when it was succeeded by the rifle musket.

In dimensions, it was an exact mate of the Model 1835, the flintlock with such a tenacious existence. All the difference lay in the lock. The complicated flintlock hammer had disappeared, and in its place was an almost equally large but much simpler hammer, a large metal affair with a spur for cocking and its front end hollowed out to enclose the percussion cap and nipple as it struck them. Gone too were the pan, frizzen, and the large V-shaped frizzen spring. The barrel had a metal bolster mounted in the former location of the touch hole, and from the top of the bolster protruded the cylindrical square-base nipple.

The lock plate, flat and bevel-edged, was 6.25 inches long and 1.25 inches wide. It was marked in front of the hammer with a spread eagle facing rearward and behind the hammer with the word Springfield and the date in three vertical lines.

The walnut stock was of the same pattern as the flintlock from which it was taken, 55 inches long, and held to the barrel by three brightly polished iron bands. The bands were styled after those of the flintlock, a large two-strap upper band, with the space between the straps cut in an ornamental curve; the middle band held the upper sling swivel, and the lower band swept out to a wide flare at the bottom. The lower two bands were held in place by springs in front of each band.

All metalwork was polished bright, including the 42-inch-round barrel, which was marked with the standard V, P, and eagle's head.

Alterations from Flintlock to Percussion

AS the percussion system eclipsed the flintlock arms, the Army found itself the owner of an amazing collection of obsolete firearms. Concurrently with the manufacture of percussion muskets and rifles, the

Government arsenals began converting flintlocks to the percussion system. Luckily the job was not difficult and could be done in any number of ways. Since the first cap and ball weapons were designed from flintlock actions, the entire lock mechanism on either gun was much the same, and a flintlock could be converted to cap and ball by removing the hammer, pan, frizzen, and frizzen spring, and replacing the old hammer with one built to fire a percussion cap. The conversion left the lock plate with a lot of empty screw holes in it, none of which affected functioning at all, though most of the Army conversions were finished by plugging the holes with brass. This left only the barrel to be considered.

In the main, there were three systems used in converting the barrels of flintlock muskets to cap and ball. In the first, the side touch hole in the barrel was filled with metal and a hole was drilled into the top of the barrel; the hole was tapped and threaded, and a percussion nipple screwed into it, and the musket was ready to go.

The second method, sometimes called the drum and nipple conversion, consisted of a hollow cylinder screwed into the location of the original touch hole. Into this cylinder or drum, which extended from the barrel at right angles to the long axis of the bore, was screwed a standard percussion nipple.

The third method was a little more elaborate, requiring a sort of rounded metal bolster to be brazed onto the side of the barrel, in the location of the touch hole. A hole was drilled into the bolster, and threaded to take a percussion nipple.

There were other methods used in making percussion guns out of flintlocks; there was one thing you could say about conversion—anything would work. A few conversions even retained the old flintlock hammer by substituting a small metal cylinder for the flint. As the hammer fell forward the cylinder smashed the cap well enough to fire the weapon.

U.S. Rifle, Model 1841

THE death knell of the flintlock was sounded in 1841, although its manufacture actually continued until 1848. But after watching

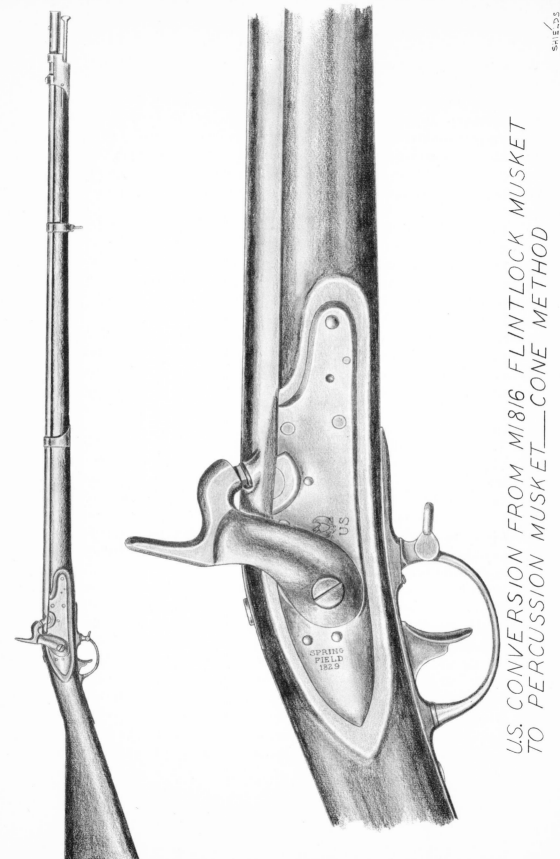

U.S. CONVERSION FROM M1816 FLINTLOCK MUSKET
TO PERCUSSION MUSKET___CONE METHOD

SPRING
FIELD
1829

the percussion system rise in stature for twenty-five years, the Ordnance Department decided there might be something to it after all, and got off to a flying start in 1841, with a muzzle-loading rifle designed for use with the percussion cap. It was a good one, well-designed, superbly finished, and as handy a percussion rifle as one could conceivably find. Because of its effectiveness, it was known at first as the Jäger rifle, after the German word for hunter. Six years later it was called the Mississippi rifle, in honor of the Mississippi Rifle Regiment commanded by Jefferson Davis. If they only knew.

The Model 1841 rifle was made principally at Harpers Ferry, although Springfield turned them out in limited quantity. It was a caliber .54 rifle, about 49 inches long. As on all the percussion rifles, the combination flat and convex lock plate of the flintlock was discarded and the lock plate was a flat forging with beveled edges, 5.25 inches long by 1.25 inches wide. It was marked in front of the hammer with a spread eagle facing rearwards, surmounting the letters U.S. Behind the hammer were the words Harpers Ferry and the date of manufacture in three vertical lines. The entire hammer surface was convexly rounded, and like the lock plate, was case hardened in mottled grey colors. The lock was inletted into the stock, to bevel height in the walnut stock, a conventional design with a comb and no pistol grip. A brass patch box was set into the right side of the buttstock.

The barrel was rifled with seven grooves which made one revolution in 72 inches. It was circular in cross section, coated with brown lacquer, and was fitted with a fixed rear sight and a brass blade front sight. Two musket-type brass bands held the stock to the barrel, both were locked into place by band springs. The upper band spring had a stud which protruded into a corresponding hole in the body of the band. With the exception of polished iron swivels, all furniture was made of brass, trigger guard, butt plate, patch box, and barrel bands.

The rifle was originally designed to handle a prefabricated paper cartridge containing seventy-five grains of black powder and a pre-patched spherical lead bullet. In the early 1850's the Minié bullet found its way over to the United States, and most of the existing Model 1841 rifles were recalled to the armories, where they were rebored and rerifled to caliber .58, taking the Minié ball of subsequent Civil War fame, the combination of a paper cartridge, caliber .58 hollow base bullet, and fifty grains of black powder.

The rifles so altered were also equipped with an adjustable rear sight and a stud for mounting a 22.5-inch saber bayonet. Since this rifle was manufactured for service issue for about fourteen years, it may be found with any

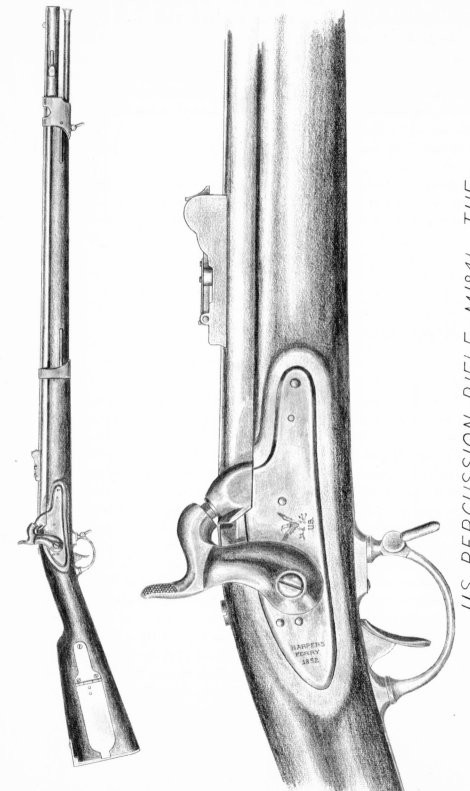

U.S. PERCUSSION RIFLE, M1841 — THE JÄGER OR MISSISSIPPI RIFLE

of a number of variations. The sights may be either fixed, or of a two-leaf type, or adjustable by means of a sliding ramp. As originally issued, the rifle had no provision for mounting a bayonet. Subsequent bayonet mounts were of three main types; a stud affixed to the right side of the barrel, a notch and groove arrangement on the barrel, or simply a bayonet which locked around the barrel with a split ring and a screw which compressed the ring around the barrel by friction.

The Model 1841 was also made under private contract by Remington, Robbins and Lawrence, Tryon, and Whitney.

The specimen illustrated was made at Harpers Ferry in 1852, and is bored to caliber .58 and fitted with an adjustable rear sight and a bayonet stud on the right side of the barrel between the upper band and the muzzle.

U.S. Rifle Musket, Model 1855

THE invention of the Minié bullet paved the way for a notable advance in the combat effectiveness of military rifles. It was adopted by our forces in 1855, and the best of our existing rifles were rebored and rerifled for its use. The change led Jefferson Davis, at that time our Secretary of War, to order the manufacture of a new model rifle specifically designed for use with the new loading system. In addition to the Minié bullet, Davis had another trick up his sleeve, a magazine-fed primer system. Military men, though slow to recognize the phenomenal advantage of the metallic percussion cap, quickly became aware of its major limitation in the field—it was hard to handle. After powder and ball had been rammed down a rifle barrel, the shooter had to extract one diminutive cap from a box of loose ones, thumb the hammer back to half cock, and fit the cap over the nipple. It was apparent that a rifle which would prime itself before each shot could obviate the difficulties which went hand in hand with single percussion caps.

Within the space of four years, several mechanical primer systems were patented, only two of which ever enjoyed wide application. These were the Lawrence primer system, used on the Sharps rifle, and the Maynard tape primer.

The newly adopted magazine primer system, which was to have troubles of its own, was the invention of Dr. Edward Maynard, a Washington dentist. The primer was made up of two long strips of paper glued together, with small globs of fulminate of mercury sandwiched between the strips at regular intervals. The result was a man-sized version of the rolls of paper caps used in today's toy cap pistols. The strips were varnished to waterproof them, but varnish or no varnish, moisture seepage was to prove their undoing. A circular recess, which served as a primer magazine, was drilled into the lock plate of every weapon adapted for use with the tape primer. A hinged metal plate closed over the recess after the coiled strip of caps was put in place. Each time the hammer was cocked, a small spring-actuated pawl pushed the tape forward, placing one primer over the nipple, where it was discharged by the falling hammer.

Besides manufacturing a new rifle, the Government went all out for the tape primer, and contracted with Remington Arms Company to alter thousands of flintlock muskets to the Maynard system. The Remington alteration lock differed only in minute detail from the original Maynard lock. In the writer's collection is one of these beauties, a Model 1816 flintlock fitted with a new lock and a caliber .69 smoothbore barrel to which had been affixed, in a burst of boundless optimism, a rear sight graduated for 400 yards. The musket itself was lucky to shoot that far.

It was about this time that the practice of making rifles and muskets in two different lengths caught up with us, for we manufactured a Model 1855 rifle, caliber .58, about 50 inches long, and also put out a Model 1855 rifle, caliber .58, about 60 inches long. The two arms had converged, producing not rifle and carbine, but two long shoulder arms of only slightly differing lengths. The longer of the two, the big production item, was called a rifle musket, a shoulder arm bored to rifle caliber but retaining the outside dimensions of the musket. The rifle, though only 10 inches shorter, was apparently considered to be a sort of specialized subsidiary weapon. Convention is sometimes hard to shake off.

The Model 1855 rifle musket was a caliber .58 muzzle-loader a full 5 feet long. The percussion lock was of standard type, except for the tape primer mechanism which held a roll of fifty percussion caps. The lock plate, 5.5 inches long by 1.9 inches wide, was flat, bevel-edged, and was stamped with the letters U.S., and the armory name, Springfield, in front of the primer magazine. The magazine cover was marked with a spread eagle, and the date of manufacture was stamped behind the hammer.

The stock had a conventional comb and a butt plate with a deep con-

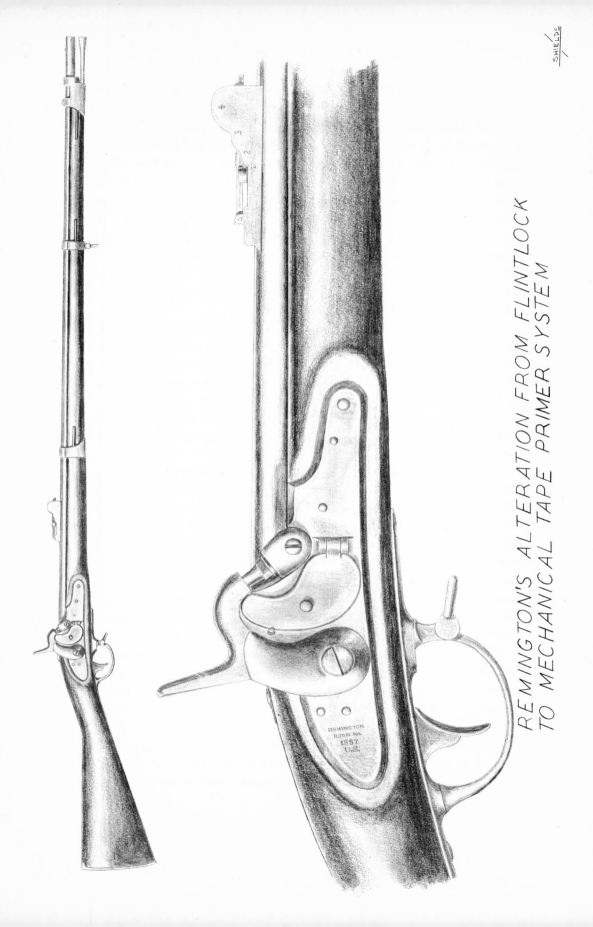

REMINGTON'S ALTERATION FROM FLINTLOCK
TO MECHANICAL TAPE PRIMER SYSTEM

cave curve. From 1855 until 1859, the stock had no patch box; thereafter there was a change, and existing specimens may be either plain or fitted with an iron patch box on the right side of the buttstock. The stock was held to the barrel by three plain flat bands which were anchored in position by band springs forward of each band. The large upper band of older muskets was discarded and the front end of the stock was protected by an iron fore end cap. The 40-inch-round barrel was rifled with three grooves with a twist of one turn in 72 inches, bored to fit the Minié bullet, a five-hundred grain cylindroconoidal bullet powered along by sixty grains of black powder. The barrel had an adjustable leaf-type rear sight until 1858, when the two-leaf Civil War type was approved.

U.S. Rifle, Model 1855

THE Model 1855 rifle, manufactured at Harpers Ferry, was a sort of stubby version of the Model 1855 rifle musket; other than the difference in barrel lengths, there were no important variations between the two weapons. The locks resembled each other closely enough to be virtually interchangeable, and were it not for the difference in armory names, one could pass for the other. Like the rifle musket, the Model 1855 rifle was finished by polishing; there was no chemical finish whatsoever. The rifle's barrel was 33 inches to the rifle musket's 40 inches, though the twist of the rifling was the same for each arm, one turn in 6 feet. For reasons best known to the Army, the rifle, the shorter weapon of the two, had the most accurate sighting equipment.

Due to its shorter stock, the barrel of the Model 1855 rifle was held to the stock by two plain iron bands, seated in place by band springs forward of each band. The front end of the stock was protected by an iron fore end cap, and the right side of the buttstock mounted the usual iron patch box on its right side.

Both the Model 1855 rifle and rifle musket had a short manufacturing history. Within six years after their adoption, the Army junked the mechanical primer system and returned to the single percussion cap.

U. S. Rifle Musket, Model 1861

THOUGH it was not realized at the time, the Government began producing in 1861 a rifle musket which was soon to be turned out by the hundreds of thousands as the main fighting tool of the Civil War. Field reports concerning the Maynard tape primer indicated that it would probably be a combat failure. It worked well in dry weather but dampness simply negated it. When the decision was made to drop the Maynard system the Ordnance Department returned to the normal copper percussion cap which gave consistent, dependable, though unspectacular performance.

All in all, the Model 1861 rifle musket was no great change from the Model 1855, except that it no longer had a primer magazine. It fired the same serviceable caliber .58 Minié bullet, and was of musket length, 56 inches long. The lock plate, flat, bevel-edged, and brightly polished, was 5.4 inches long by 1.25 inches wide. The lock mechanism was of good but undistinguished design, a perfected version of the same lock we had been using since 1795. The lock plate was stamped with the letters U.S., and the word Springfield, and the spread eagle. The date was behind the hammer.

The butt plate, bent in a crescent curve, was attached to a simple low-combed walnut stock. The stock was held to the barrel by three plain iron bands, each of which was secured by band springs in front of each band. An iron fore end cap protected the front end of the stock. The 40-inch-round barrel was rifled with three grooves which made one turn in 72 inches, the standard twist for that caliber. The sights were of the simple two-leaf type common to most of our Civil War weapons. The nipple cone had a cleanout screw in its right side.

Harpers Ferry Armory, which had been seized briefly in John Brown's abortive rebellion, was one of the first casualties of the Civil War, and the sudden burden placed on Springfield Armory was far beyond that armory's capacity to produce. The Government turned, as it always must, to a number of private firms in order to equip the Army. However, this was no Keystone Cops Comedy of regimented inefficiency, such as the Revolution had

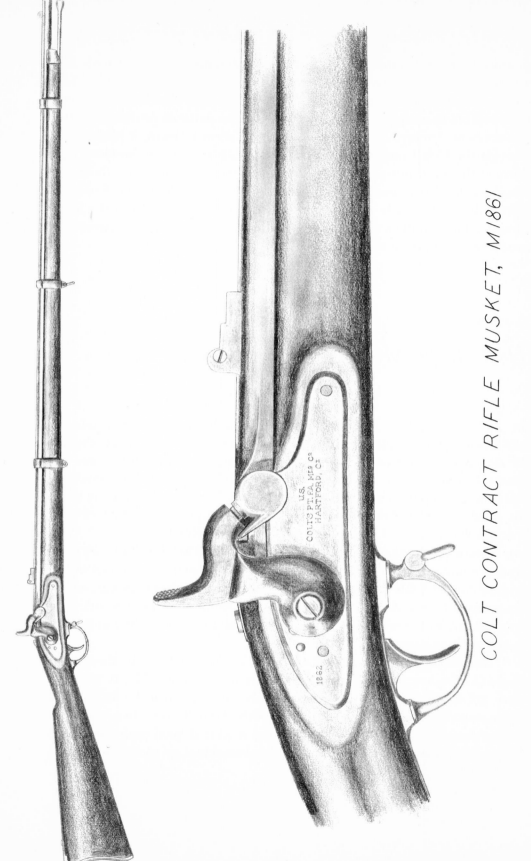

COLT CONTRACT RIFLE MUSKET, M1861

U.S.
COLT'S PT. FA. MFG. CO
HARTFORD, CT

1862

SHIELDS

produced. American industry, with its preponderance of machine tools and assembly line methods, was well suited to turning out weapons of war. The contract weapons with which Union troops were armed were without exception well-made weapons, exact duplicates of the patterns provided by the Government Armory. But, and this we never seem to learn, it takes time. Though the Colt Company alone eventually made over one hundred and thirteen thousand muzzle-loading rifles and almost four hundred thousand revolvers, the Government was forced to purchase shoulder arms from the British during the early days of the war in order to put troops in the field. Almost a half a million Enfield rifle muskets were bought before American production caught up with the job assigned to it.

U.S. Rifle Musket, Model 1863

EARLY in 1863, a new model rifle musket was introduced into manufacture, a slightly simplified version of the Model 1861, though for all practical purposes it was the same weapon. The chief differences between the two were for the most part of negative quality, a few eliminations intended to simplify manufacture; several parts were dropped, among them the band springs and the cleanout screw in the nipple cone. The lockwork was case hardened and most of the metalwork was blued.

Before production was well under way, the Model 1863 underwent several additional changes which brought it back to about the design of the original Model 1861. The stock was again inletted for band springs, as the unanchored bands of the Model '63 tended to work loose from recoil. The dovetail slot for the rear sight was eliminated, and the rear sight was held to the barrel by a pair of machine screws.

This was the last muzzle-loading arm to be manufactured by the United States Government, marking the end of a seventy-year era. Military weapons were still relatively crude, but immeasurably advanced over the first United States muzzle-loaders that were made in 1795. Actually, only two important design changes had been made. Flint and steel had been replaced by the copper percussion cap and the smoothbore barrel had given way to a rifled

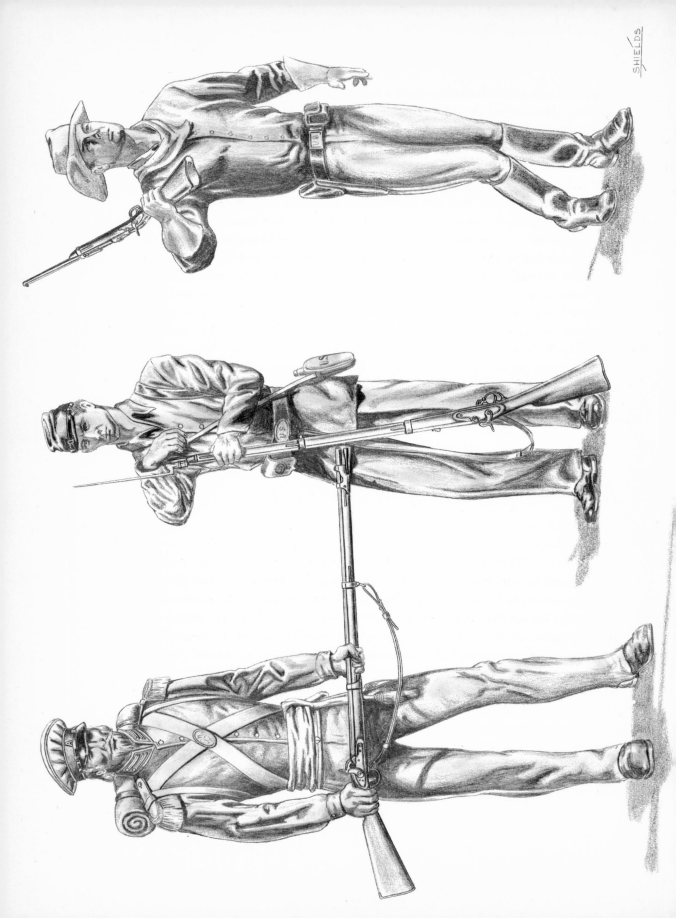

barrel, for which had been designed a bullet which could make optimum use of rifling. It made all the difference in the world. Out of an ancient German hunting arm, out of the inventions of a Scottish Minister and a French Army captain came a rifle whose effective range was measured in hundreds of yards and which could be relied upon in good weather or bad. And whatever it hit stayed hit. The age of the ultra-velocity small-caliber-jacketed bullet was yet to come, and the rifle musket achieved its purpose, the infliction of damage upon enemy personnel, by means of five hundred grains of soft lead which, in its own outmoded way, was murderously effective. It was forced out of the muzzle at considerable velocity, and would make a puncture wound in excess of a half inch in diameter. If it encountered sudden resistance, such as bone, it would either upset or lose the stability imparted to it by its rotation and gyrate wildly about its own axis like a spinning top which has suddenly been tipped over, producing the dreadful wounds which maimed so many Civil War veterans. Warfare was getting bigger, involving more and more men, killing more men at longer ranges, and crippling more. It was to get worse.

Rifle Musket, Bayonet, and Tactics

THE Civil War was the biggest war our country had as yet fought, and by all odds the most devastating in our history, a dreadful example of multiple fratricide, like a fight to the death among the crew of the same ship; for all the fighting took place within our own borders, amidst appalling battle attrition. It was a war which enabled one of its generals to boast that any crow which flew over the Shenandoah Valley would have to carry its own rations. Those few design changes made in the interval between 1795 and 1861 had proved to be of immeasurable importance. First of all, the flintlock and all thought of using it had passed out of existence. The copper percussion cap was firmly implanted as the standard method of ignition. The smoothbore barrel had gone the way of the mace and the broadsword; military-issue weapons were all rifled. On the experimental level, metallic cartridges had appeared, and breech-loading and even magazine rifles had begun to take shape in inventors' workshops and factories. For weapons had been progressing in the direction they always must, tending to strike harder, more rapidly, and at greater ranges than the ones before them. On the other hand, traditional tactical employment of weapons remained as it had been in the day of the smoothbore musket, while the improved firearms used in such employment demanded change and innovation. The progress of one and the inanition of the other left a dangerous tactical gap which troop commanders had to bridge or lose their units in battle. The rifle was no stranger to combat, but there had never been a first class war in which both sides were armed with it; its effect upon combat formations was largely unknown, although the Battle of New Orleans should have given someone a hint. But a few obscure rifle victories notwithstanding, infantry had always served as a group of glorified spear carriers; they were armed with a musket good for one quick shot, to which was affixed a long skewer-like bayonet. The idea was to advance through one or two volleys of inaccurate fire and close in with bare steel, relying on the weight and shock of the assault to carry the defenders' positions. This was fine, provided the assault element survived the crossing of the fire-swept space separating the two forces. Against the musket, it could be done. The musket's pitifully short range and general inefficiency permitted it. But if the defenders' weapons could be made to fire far enough and often enough, the day would come when any massed charge, no matter how gallant, would be broken before it reached the defending army's positions. The rifle saw the dawn of many such days. Firepower was to be crowned king of the battlefield, though few realized it at the onset of the war.

As in World War I, where a similar anachronism between weapons and the methods of employing them was present, armies learned painfully, amid screams and blood, a simple lesson—that increased fire power puts all the odds in favor of a determined defender. The enlisted recruits died by the thousands under galling, raking rifle fire before their commanders became aware of the method of remedying combat losses which decimated entire regiments in short convulsive battles of less than a day's duration. This is not to say that the defending, that is the weaker side, is liable to win. Not at all. An army may attack on a strategic level, and yet defend in the sense that it meets enemy movement by massed fire from covered positions.

This total lack of ability to meet the requirements of increased firepower was really not the fault of the standing army, as such. During the Mexican and Indian wars, the Army had developed the wide open skirmishing principles which were infinitely far advanced over those used in contemporary European armies. But almost a third of the Army's Officer Corps, apparently the better third at that, had resigned to join their secessionist states; and the bulk of the wartime Union Army officers knew nothing whatsoever about fighting, at least when they took command of their units. For at the outbreak of that unhappy war, whoever rounded up the necessary troops (and this usually took a great deal of money) got a colonel's commission, command of a regiment, and after receiving a pat on the head and the blessing of some state governor, headed off for the high jinks of wartime Washington. It made good political patronage and made the fighting a living horror. When we consider that the Union Army began the war with about six hundred officers and that the same Army eventually received almost three million enlistments, we are forced to the conclusion that a considerable portion of the Army was unaware of the necessity for changes made mandatory by the appearance of rifled arms.

All the old theories fell to pieces. Yet workable or not, they were the only ones known to the majority of troop commanders, which in part accounts for the enormous percentage of casualties per engagement, battles in which the victor's ranks were too depleted to allow him to follow up his advantage.

The Civil War lasted for four years, and comprised many campaigns and dozens of battles of unequaled ferocity. It is beyond the scope of this book to even attempt to furnish an outline of the progress of that war. What is important to us is this, the realization that weapons and tactics are both tied together by the same piece of string, and a change in one must be accompanied by a compensating change in the other. Assault under direct rifle fire was at best likely to produce a Pyrrhic victory. Even artillery, often the decisive factor in infantry engagements, was forced into a new role. In a musket-dominated war, cannons could be placed right up with the infantry, where grape and canister shot were used as giant shotguns to blow a hole in the enemy formations to create a weak point vulnerable to assault. The rifle put an end to all that; its long range fire could easily pick off artillery gunners and crewmen, and artillery, though capable of longer range fire than its predecessor, the Napoleonic muzzle-loader, was driven into a position far behind its own infantry, where continued support in a fast-moving situation became impossible.

The bayonet charge eventually became a rarity. It could be ripped apart like rotten fabric, as defending troops learned that, if you were close enough to stick the enemy you were certainly close enough to shoot him. Assault in the grand manner simply ceased to be; bravery and willingness to die were no longer enough, though they were drawn on time and again. A pretty good idea of the textbook bayonet charge, all done according to the rules, was made by Union infantry at Antietam. The assault was made across a wide front, men walking side by side and four deep, four long skirmish lines with the front rank holding its rifles at "charge bayonets," and the other three at "right shoulder lift." The commander, on horseback, was in front of the lead rank. A military band whooped up martial enthusiasm, and the entire advance was made in step to the tocsin beat of a military drum. Much like leading cattle to a slaughter house. General Packenham's redcoats at New Orleans could not have been more achingly gallant, nor chosen a worse method of advancing, and the back of the effort was broken in a matter of minutes. But slowly, with almost agonizing slowness, commanders and troops alike began to catch on, and developed the only tactics capable of success under the limitations imposed by the above conditions. Just as one can witness a modern battle and come away with the impression that it was nothing so much as a bunch of men talking into field telephones, one would not recognize a late phase Civil War battle from the popular conception of one. The infantry had learned that enemy fire power had to be overwhelmed by friendly fire before direct movement against it was possible, and that one did not charge in a concerted rush. A "charge" broke down into small clusters of men hugging the dirt, moving forward by short rushes at widely spaced intervals, fighting desperately for insignificant elevations or depressions in the earth's surface, rushing forward only when the superiority of covering fire gave them something of a chance. When so engaged a weaker force could either hold on and die, or give way foot by foot. And battles became such see-saw ordeals wherein a now nonexistent rail fence on a backwoods farm would become the focal point where men, with terrible selflessness, gave their lives for reasons they hardly understood.

Breech-Loading Percussion Arms

FROM the first there were many things wrong with the whole principle of loading a shoulder arm from the muzzle end. A man in combat, subjected to the most unbelievable excesses of fear, excitement, and fatigue, can usually be relied upon to do the wrong thing and bring out any failings inherent in a mechanical system. Muzzle-loading can only with the greatest charity be described as slow. By the time of the Civil War, over five centuries after the first crude muzzle-loading weapons were invented, it still took something like nine separate operations to prepare the military shoulder arm for firing. And quite apart from being slow, muzzle-loading had several disastrous limitations. It was almost impossible to load a muzzle-loader in any position except standing or kneeling. The soldier suffered a paralyzing naked exposure to enemy fire every time he loaded his weapon, and he stood a good chance of lacerating his right hand on the bayonet while doing so. The business of reloading became a paramount issue in the soldier's mind, so much so that thousands of battlefield relics have been found with several loads, one on top the other, without any of them having been fired, for a muzzle-loader gave no outside indication of whether it was loaded or empty. It was the result of the troops concentrating on loading to the exclusion of everything else, including firing, and stemmed from buck fever, the same adrenalin-born illogical conduct which manifests itself when a novice hunter drops his rifle and tears after game with his bare hands. It can never be eliminated, but the less complicated the system, the less likely it is to show up. The necessity for speedy reloading often led excitement-consumed troops to pull the trigger before every necessary step in the involved reloading procedure was completed, resulting in misfires or freak accidents. A man might fire before he removed the ramrod from the barrel, and watch in horrified embarrassment as his reloading tool went arcing across the enemy lines. Or, if required to fire several rounds from one position, he would stick the ramrod in the ground, for easy accessibility, and then walk off without it as his unit advanced or retreated. This left him with an inefficient spear until he found a new ramrod. Or suppose he would ram the bullet down before the powder charge; *that* would fix him for the remainder of the battle.

The metallic cartridge, which eliminated most of these troubles, was soon to be developed, but not before several percussion breech-loaders were invented and adopted by our forces as secondary weapons, to be used with varying degrees of success.

Colt Percussion Breech-Loading Rifle, Model 1855

THE first of our percussion breech-loaders, other than the Hall percussion conversion, was a six-shot repeater manufactured by the Colt Company and used in limited quantity during the Civil War. The Colt handgun was an outstanding success and seemed to be a natural basis for the design of a rifle which would be a repeating arm as well as a breech-loader. So why not a revolving rifle?

It is hard to realize that a rifle, so sound in fundamental concept, could be such a flat failure in actual use. But the Colt rifle simply wasn't safe to shoot. As a safety feature, all the nipples on the cylinder were separated by wide metal partitions whose functions were to confine each explosion and prevent the ignition of more than one chamber at a time. But gas leakage, faulty caps and stray powder grains which would often spill through the rear of the large nipples all conspired to prove otherwise. At such times, when the shooter pulled the trigger, there would be a colossal report, a spray of metal fragments, and the good possibility of the loss of an eye or hand. Troops will accept the possibility of being maimed, but not the certainty of it, and by their own weapons at that.

Even if the rifle held together and only one chamber fired, there was nothing to be happy about. For the Colt rifle, and I hate to seem redundant about this, leaked gas. So did the revolver, but the two cases were entirely different. The Colt rifle was essentially an over-sized-revolver action with a stock and a long barrel; any revolver, the modern ones included, leak gas as the bullet crosses the gap between the front of the cylinder and the breech end of the barrel. It is not noticeable, because in the normal grip for a revolver the hand is behind the cylinder and the whole weapon is held some distance from the face. In a revolving rifle the conditions are reversed. The cylinder is close to the face and the left arm, used to steady the rifle, is near the open end of the cylinder. Add to that the burst of the percussion cap

[82]

near the shooter's eyes and the possibility that all chambers might let go at once, and one can easily see why the Colt system, while an enormous success in handguns, was as a rifle never popular with the troops to whom it was issued. Yet had the Colt rifle been a success, there was an old guard criticism ready and waiting for it, a military criticism leveled at any repeating or magazine rifle. It is an old idea, used in condemning every rapid fire weapon from the bow and arrow upwards; and it's enough to make one shudder. In brief, the theory held that soldiers armed with repeating weapons would tend to waste expensive ammunition by firing at everything in sight, rather than waiting to fire the one round they knew their lives depended on. Such critics invariably forgot that the duty of a soldier was not to die for his cause, but to make the enemy die for his. But by the time a man became hidebound enough to think that way, he had often worked his way up to a position of some importance in the military, and his presence and the exercise of his opinions served as a continuous sea anchor on any move forward.

The Colt rifle was a caliber .44 six-shooter, an outgrowth of Colt's revolving pistol. Like the revolver, its firing chambers were bored in a cylinder which rotated about a central axial pin, so that each cocking of the hammer served to rotate the cylinder through one-sixth of a circle and align a fresh load with the breech end of the barrel. Unlike the revolver, its hammer was on the side of the frame instead of directly behind the cylinder. The structural weakness of the Colt revolver lay in its open top frame; the heavy rifle demanded a solid frame, and the hammer was shifted to allow for it.

The revolving rifle was loaded like the conventional revolver of its day; into each chamber of the cylinder was placed a combustible paper cartridge containing powder and ball; the hammer was placed at half-cock and the cylinder was rotated one chamber at a time until the nose of the bullet was beneath the rammer of the loading lever, located under the barrel. A downward pull on the lever seated the bullet to its proper depth in the chamber. The operation was repeated for each chamber; a percussion cap was placed on each nipple, and the rifle was ready for business. If prefabricated nitrate-treated paper cartridges were unavailable, one could pour loose powder and individual bullets into the chambers, just as on the revolver.

All told, a splendid system, just completely out of its element in weapons of rifle size. In its limited military use, it was regarded as a specialized arm. Colonel Berdan's sharpshooters, the First and Second regiments, were armed with the Colt rifles before the Colonel wrangled Sharps rifles for issue to his men.

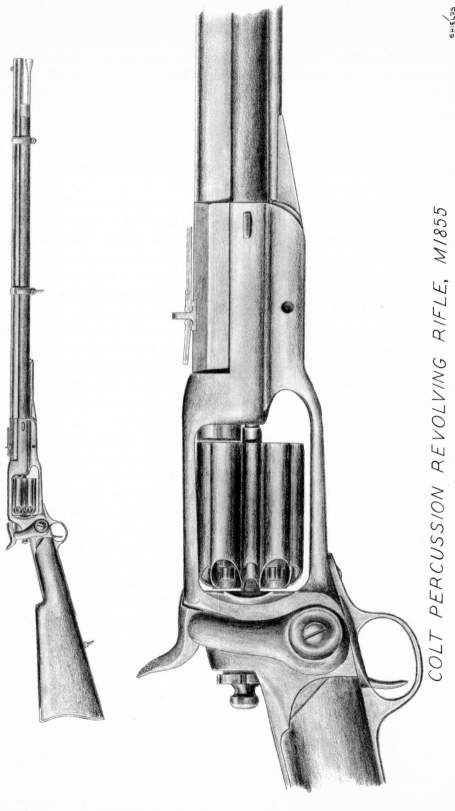

COLT PERCUSSION REVOLVING RIFLE, M1855

In infantry size, the rifle had a cylindrical barrel 31.3 inches long, rifled with seven grooves. The stock was made in two pieces, a buttstock and a fore arm which was held to the barrel by two blued-steel bands. All metal parts, with the exception of the case-hardened hammer and loading lever, were blued to inhibit rusting. The Colt military rifles were made in several calibers and barrel lengths, among them calibers .56, .50, .44, and .40. The barrels ranged from 24-inch carbines to the 31.3-inch barrel of the full length rifle. Depending on the caliber of the arm, the cylinder capacity was five or six cartridges.

Credit for the first successful design and manufacture of the revolving firearms properly belongs to Samuel Colt of Hartford, Connecticut, certainly one of the most flamboyant figures in firearms history. The fundamental idea for a revolving firearm was old, as most basic conceptions are old, but Colt was the first man to make a successful go of it. The percussion cap was the key to Colt's success, for it made feasible a design which was unsuccessful when employed with flint and steel ignition. Colt's basic patents, taken out in England, covered a revolver with a six-toothed rachet built onto the rear end of the cylinder. When the hammer was thumbed back, a metal pawl attached to the hammer pushed the rachet through an arc sufficient to align one chamber with the barrel, where it was held in position by a spring-operated cylinder bolt. The rear of the cylinder was built into a series of six nipples, each separated by a thick metal partition.

As a young man, Colt founded the Patent Arms Company of Paterson, New Jersey, where he produced several of the now-rare Paterson models before the whole venture came to an end in 1842, a thumping financial failure. It was the Mexican War which gave Colt his needed boost. The privately owned Paterson Colts which saw service on the front were so sought after that Colt was given a contract for the manufacture of one thousand revolving pistols. Colt had no factory in which to fulfill the contract, and the revolvers were made at Eli Whitney's plant at Whitneyville, Connecticut. Thereafter, the westward expansion of the nation's newly-acquired territory and the Civil War provided Colt with an almost unlimited market for the weapon whose production was a virtual Colt monopoly.

Sharps Breech-Loading Percussion Rifle, Model 1859

ONE of the few successful percussion breech-loaders was one of the first ones put on the market, a rifle invented by Christian Sharps in 1848. Though a single-shot rifle, it was held in higher esteem by the troops to whom it was issued than the Colt revolving rifle, a six-shot repeater. The original Sharps rifle was strictly a commercial venture, never seeing military service in the United States Army until after it had been perfected to a considerable degree. Sharps rifles were sold to all comers, Great Britain and Mexico being among the purchasers of large lots of Sharps cavalry carbines. When later manufactured for use with heavy caliber metallic cartridges, the Sharps became a great favorite with plainsmen and buffalo hunters, and while never the standard Army issue weapon, it was employed with enormous success by regiments whose specialty was scouting and sniping. The most famous of these outfits were commanded by Colonel Post and Colonel Hiram Berdan, a remarkable soldier-inventor whose fame today rests on the invention of the center-fire cartridge primer bearing his name. It was Berdan who managed to secure Sharps breech-loaders for his riflemen despite the bitter opposition of General Winfield Scott and the Chief of Ordnance, General Ripley, who seemed to consider the breech-loader as somewhat immoral.

The Sharps rifle had a simple and well-conceived locking system, a heavy metal block which slid vertically in a pair of mortises. The system was eventually supplanted by magazine rifle designs, but virtually all the world's present-day field artillery operates on the Sharps principle. The breech block was lowered by pushing forward a finger lever which served as a trigger guard, exposing the chamber for loading with a linen cartridge. The return of the lever to its closed position lifted the breech block behind the chamber. As the breech block rose to its locked position, its sharp upper edge sheared off the rear end of the fabric cartridge and allowed it to be

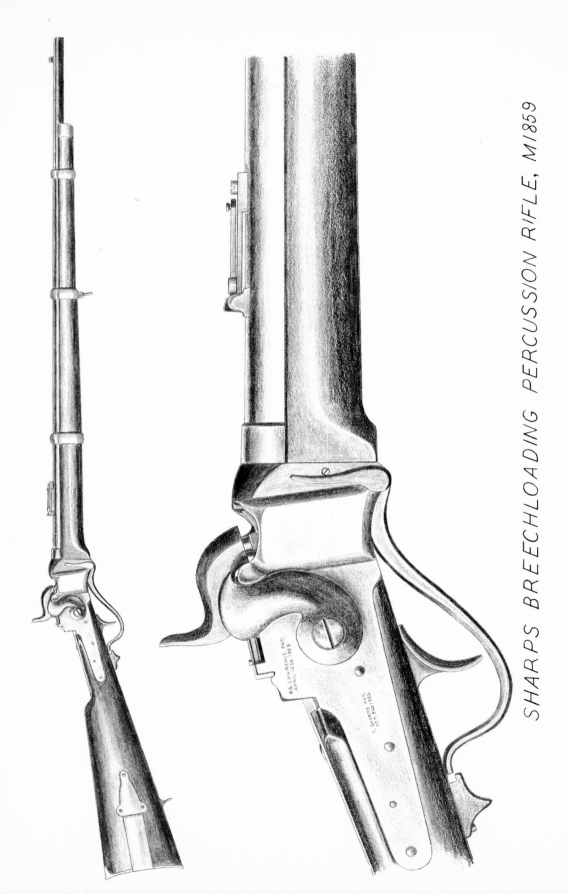

SHARPS BREECHLOADING PERCUSSION RIFLE, M1859

SHIELDS

R.S. LAWRENCE PAT.
APRIL 12TH 1859

C. SHARPS PAT.
OCT. 5TH 1852

ignited by a percussion cap placed on the nipple of the breech block. In order to reduce loss of gas at the breech, the face of the breech block was provided with an expanding ring gascheck, considerably reducing the flash-backs which were the bane of percussion breech-loaders. The side hammer had to be cocked manually and was entirely independent of any motion of the breech block. After the cartridge had been loaded, the hammer was thumbed back, and its rearward motion automatically fed a primer onto the nipple from a primer magazine located on the right side of the receiver. The primers were issued in small brass tubes which were used to charge the primer magazine fifty pellets at a time. A primer magazine cutoff allowed the shooter to hold his primers in reserve and prime the rifle with conventional percussion caps. This coil spring-fed-magazine was the invention of R. S. Lawrence, armorer for the Sharps Company's Hartford plant.

The model selected for adoption by the infantry was a caliber .52 rifle with a 3-foot-round barrel, rifled with six grooves. The two-piece walnut stock was of the full length military type with a patch box on the right side of the buttstock and an iron fore end cap. It was held to the barrel by three oval iron bands. The sighting equipment was of the sort common to many later day military rifles, a blade front sight and a ladder-type leaf rear sight graduated from 100 to 800 yards.

The lock plate was marked in two sets of horizontal lines, C. Sharps pat. Oct. 5th, 1852; and R. S. Lawrence Pat. April 12th, 1859. The left side of the receiver was stamped C. Sharps Pat. Sept. 12th, 1848. The Sharps was also made in 30-inch barrel length; this one was called the New Model 1859, and was so stamped on the receiver.

The Sharps rifle was famous, and justly so, for its performance during the Civil War, but its great notoriety stems from its use in the squabbles over the slavery question in Kansas. During the 1850's Kansas became the focal point of the slavery problem and was occupied and supported by peo-ple who held equally militant views on opposite sides of the same question. Nothing but trouble could and did result from it. For a while Kansas was the scene of an internal civil war and many Sharps carbines, bought commer-cially with funds collected from abolitionists all over the nation, were shipped to Kansas as more fuel for the fire. Some of them arrived in crates labeled Bibles, and Sharps carbines became known as Beecher's Bibles, after a prominent anti-slavery preacher.

But one morning in 1859, the Sharps carbine came with terrible swift-ness into national prominence as the weapon used in John Brown's raid and capture of Harpers Ferry Arsenal.

Brown was a peculiar sort, with the appearance of a biblical prophet, and was imbued with a full-blown Messianic complex, one of those persons of tremendous and totally intemperate moral persuasion who believed that cruelty and bloodshed could be made right by more cruelty and more bloodshed. Some of the Sharps carbines consigned for use in Kansas were diverted from that state as peace and order were restored, and they were turned over to Brown, one of the leading abolitionist fighters, for safekeeping. Just what he needed. Early on the morning of October 16, 1859, Brown's followers, after having signed their own provisional constitution, swept into the arsenal and captured it without resistance. That was phase one. The man's overall plan seemed to have been to commandeer the weapons and ammunition stored at Harpers Ferry and use them as a stockpile for arming his proposed slave rebellion throughout the South. Brown announced that he was there in the name of Jehovah, took a group of hostages, established a ring of sentries, and waited. By noon of the same day, United States troops were on their way to the arsenal, under command of Colonel Robert E. Lee, second in command, Lieutenant J. E. B. Stuart—their duty, with consummate irony, to preserve the Union.

Some militia contingent beat Lee to the arsenal, and in a sporadic rifle fight drove Brown into the arsenal engine house. During the night Lee's troops arrived, and at dawn carried the building by assault. Brown was taken to Charleston and a week later was indicted and tried for treason and conspiracy to commit treason and murder. At the trial he refused to account to anyone except his Maker; though obviously mad, he was soon given his wish. He was hanged on December 2nd. The carbines? Had Brown lived to see what became of them, the shock would have killed him. The raiders' weapons were stored at Harpers Ferry, where they were issued out to Confederate cavalry after the partially burned arsenal was overrun in the early stages of the Civil War.

The Sharps rifle waged a losing fight with magazine rifles as the years passed; in 1874, the company reorganized and shortly thereafter moved to Bridgeport, Conn., and manufactured rifles until 1881, when the firm ceased operations.

The Metallic Cartridge

THE evolution of firearms cartridges has been fully as complex as that of the weapons in which they were used, progressing through a labyrinth of various developmental stages, successes, failures, and false starts, to approach only gradually the product of today. At times, forgotten experimental cartridges have come extremely close to today's designs; sometimes they resembled nothing you ever saw.

The early firearms used no cartridge whatsoever; propellent powder, ball, wadding, and priming powder were each fed one at a time into the firearm, a state of affairs which forced the soldier to carry all the components separately and scramble through his miniature hardware store for the proper material each time he had to shoot. Rapid fire was an impossibility; the question just never came up.

By the time the flintlock came into general use, a crude cartridge had been designed for it. These early cartridges were made of paper which was wrapped around the bullet and powder charge. Their use speeded up loading considerably because the soldier no longer needed to measure out the propellant before firing each round. He bit off the end of the cartridge, poured a little powder into the pan, dumped the remainder down the barrel, rammed down the bullet, and wadded the paper on top of it. Though an improvement over the older method, paper cartridges were far from satisfactory; they were dreadfully fragile, and to guard against breakage and moisture were carried in metal boxes; and of course loading and priming were still separate operations. However, the paper musket cartridge was manufactured without change from 1795 until 1855, the year of adoption of the caliber .58 rifled musket, remaining in musket size a lead sphere .64 inches in diameter and about one hundred and thirty grains of black powder, all wrapped in paper. There was not much that could be done with it.

But while any new musket invariably resembled the model immediately preceding it, the rifle was always in a state of flux, with inventors constantly trying to alter its loading procedures, its caliber, the end of the barrel from which it was loaded, and the number of rounds it could fire upon one loading. The rifle cartridge began its history at the same level as that of the musket—zero. The Kentucky rifle shooter had not only separate propellant, ball, and priming powder to worry about, he also had a separate patch to load. The patch was usually precut to size, but some riflemen preferred to place one corner of a small sheet of fabric ovr the rifle muzzle, start the ball into the muzzle, and cut off the excess with a knife. The human nervous system being what it is, some awful miscalculations could occur at any point in the involved loading procedure during the heat of battle.

One of the first attempts to create a cartridge as we know it today, that is, one that carries with it the means for its own ignition, was made in the early part of the nineteenth century by a Swiss native named Pauli who ran a gun shop in Paris. The Pauli cartridge resembled a modern shotgun shell in that it was part paper and part metal. The cylindrical metal base was pierced in the center with a small hole into which was placed a pellet of priming compound. A normal paper cartridge was lowered into the front of the cylinder, producing a complete and unbelievably modern cartridge which required a breech-loading rifle with a hammer and striker to operate it. In 1812, it was hopelessly ahead of its time and after being turned down by the French Army, the idea was forgotten. Almost.

A German, Johann Nikolaus von Dreyse, who had worked with Pauli in Paris, went to work on his own self-igniting cartridge, and also had to design a rifle to go around it. His first patents were taken out in 1828, to cover a muzzle-loading rifle. Ten years later, in 1838, he patented a breech-loader, the *Zündnadelgewehr,* or needle rifle. The cartridge's use was confined to Prussia and France, but the rifle itself was to serve as the basis for the design of every military rifle used in World War I and most of the World War II models; it was the first bolt action rifle. The Dreyse cartridge was composed of a lead bullet to whose base was attached a disc of fulminating compound imbedded in papier mâché. The bullet, primer, and a powder charge of about seventy-five grains (which was *behind* the primer) were all wrapped in a sheet of paper. The rifle operated much like a modern bolt action rifle, even to a bolt-housed firing pin and a striker which detonated the primer, the chief difference being that the striker had to pierce the entire length of the powder charge in order to reach the primer. The firing of each round placed the striker squarely in the middle of a black powder explosion; it corroded badly and its internal crystal structure was rapidly changed by the alternate heating and cooling, breakage occurring often enough to constitute a serious defect. The rifle was also victim of the limitations of all the breech-loaders of its day—it leaked gas. But Dreyse's rifle had come extremely close to total success; all it needed was a change in primer location and a metal cartridge case. As it was, the needle rifle was adopted by the Prussians who used it to wallop the Austrians in 1866. The French adopted their own version of it, improving it to the extent of placing the primer at the base of the cartridge where it belonged. They also placed a rubber gasket inside the breech where it was forced by gas pressure to expand at the firing of each shot, sealing the breech against gas leakage. The rubber ring stood up under the explosions no better than the long needle of the Dreyse rifle, becoming non-elastic and useless after comparatively few rounds. This rifle, known as the *Chassepot*, was nonetheless better than the Prussian rifle, and the two systems locked horns in the Franco-Prussian War in 1870. By this time the pendulum of inventive thought had swung the other way, and the United States was again at the top of the pile with its lever action repeating rifles; the invention of the metallic cartridge having rendered the needle rifle and its variations as obsolete as yesterday's newspaper.

The solution to the whole business lay in the metallic cartridge case, which would not only settle the loading problem, but would solve the brain-wracking question of how to seal the breech of a breech-loading rifle. The metal cartridge case would, at one fell swoop, provide a rigid weather-proof housing for primer, propellant, and bullet, and serve as an obturator, the elastic metal expanding against the chamber walls through the force of the exploding powder, sealing the breech against gas leakage. As pressure returned to normal, the case would spring back to something like its original size, and could be easily extracted from the chamber.

But it was a long time in developing; its evolution was characterized by a long succession of cartridges, each of which represented some minor but significant improvement over its predecessor. The metallic cartridge had its inception in the work of Pauli, who had invented a cartridge before there was a successful weapon capable of handling it. But the idea of a self-contained cartridge was too sound to be abandoned. Later attempts were more successful, as the use of fulminates and percussion caps came into general acceptance.

The Lefaucheux pin-fire cartridge was one of these; the major use of this cartridge, invented about 1836, was confined chiefly to revolvers and shotguns. Like the Pauli cartridge, it consisted of a metal base and a paper tube. A pin protruded through the side of the case, its lower end resting on a percussion cap. When the pin was struck, it crushed the cap and fired the cartridge. The metal end of the case swelled violently against the walls of the chamber, forming a positive gas seal. The case was subsequently made entirely of metal and it is still in limited use today, in foreign shotguns and in obsolete revolvers of the sort manufactured for export to South America. It had two notable limitations; the protruding pin made the cartridge dangerous to handle with anything short of extreme care, and loading was slower than that of later cartridges because the pin had to be aligned in a notch in the chamber. In its day it was really not a bad system, and passed out of general use because better designs soon followed it.

A giant stride forward was taken in the 1840's with the invention of an all metal cartridge which contained its own primer. At this time the owner of a Parisian shooting gallery, Flobert, was casting about for a simple way of loading the small caliber weapons in his gallery. What he did, in essence, was to crimp a bullet into the open end of a metal percussion cap, the cap's load of fulminate of mercury serving both as primer and propellant. In practice, the cap was fitted with a flanged-base or rim to seat the cartridge to its proper depth and also to provide some purchase for extraction of the fired-case. The Flobert cartridge has been used to this day under the name of BB cap, or bulleted breech cap.

All the elements necessary for the production of a modern cartridge were now well known—the metal case, cylindrical bullet, propellant, and percussion cap; but no one had as yet put them all together into one round. The Flobert cartridges were small and had no separate propellant; the Lefaucheux cartridges had an awkward side priming and extraction system; and in America there were cartridges with metal cases which housed the bullet and propellant—trouble was, they had no primers. These weird cartridges were a sort of stopgap between paper cartridges and the self-contained metal cartridges which followed them. They were fired by separate percussion caps or by the tape primers used in the percussion military shoulder arms of the late 1850's.

In 1856, a year after his tape primer had become standard military issue, Maynard devised his externally ignited cartridge. It was a brass case containing black powder and was sealed at its forward end by a conoidal bullet. The rear end had an enormous rim pierced by a small centrally placed hole, sealed with wax. Ignition was external, the flame reaching the hole via the standard nipple and a percussion cap or tape primer. The oversized rim provided a grip for manual extraction, for there was no mechanical extractor on the weapons in which this cartridge was used.

Another military cartridge of this type was invented by General Burnside. It too was composed of a brass case, shaped like a truncated cone with the large end crimped around the bullet. The small end of the tapered case had a small aperture through which combustion was initiated. This unusual round was loaded base first into the breech block of the rifle, which tipped up and backwards for loading. Opening the breech block exposed the fired case for manual ejection. Both the Maynard and Burnside cartridges were used prior to and during the Civil War, dying out as their logical extension, the metallic cartridge with a self-contained primer, came into use.

The Civil War saw the use of all sorts of cartridges, chiefly as experimental or limited issue rounds. The mainstay of that war was the Minié paper cartridge, a caliber .58 cylindro-conoidal lead bullet weighing five hundred grains, with a hollow base and three lubricating cannelures, and sixty grains of black powder.

The completely self-contained metallic cartridge found its way into the United States as the tiny Flobert rimfire cartridge. In the 1850's, Horace Smith and Daniel Wesson experimented with a cartridge based on the Flobert BB cap, but with a view towards developing it into a healthier load. They soon found that one couldn't depend on fulminate of mercury as a propellant. It was too unstable and the consequences of each explosion were too unknown, especially in large quantities (remember Berthollet's troubles?). It also corroded steel barrels unmercifully. Smith and Wesson's solution followed the logical course of development by employing a small amount of fulminate of mercury, seated under the circumference of the rim of the cartridge case, as a primer which exploded when any portion of the rim was crushed by the hammer, and in turn ignited a main charge of black powder. Smith and Wesson had a strangle hold on metallic cartridges for handgun use, having bought in 1856, the Rollin White patent which covered revolver cylinders bored through from end to end, the only practical means of employing such a cartridge, and for a while they made the most of their advantage. Shortly after their caliber .22 rimfire appeared on the market, they put out a caliber .32 rimfire revolver and cartridge. Both of these weapons were much sought after as Civil War sidearms, in spite of their small size.

Metallic cartridges were on their way. The Civil War brought out rimfire cartridges in fairly large sizes, .38's and .41 Deringers in pistol caliber, and in rifle size, .44 and .56 rimfire rounds. The rimfire has since disappeared from use in large cartridges, but today is still made by the millions, the caliber .22 rimfire well-known to target shooters and to every boy who buys his first rifle. The rimfire round was cheap to make and gave good performance with black powder and the cartridge designs then in use. It gave way to the center-fire system because of the latter's greater safety and reliability. The rimfire could be accidentally set off by striking any part of the rim, the danger increasing as the size of the cartridge increased. The center-fire cartridge provided more certain ignition, and the later types could be reloaded with great economy by resizing the fired case, driving out the old primer, inserting a new one, and replacing propellant and bullet. The caliber .58 rimfire used in the Model 1865 Allin conversion was soon dropped in favor of the center-fire system.

The first center-fire round used in the United States Army was the folded head or inside primer type, which looked exactly like a copper case rimfire round. But it had a primer, the size of the head of the cartridge, inserted from the front end of the case and held in place by two indentations in the case about .125 inch from the head. A depression in the center of the primer cup held the priming compound, which when crushed by the firing pin, fired the round. This cartridge, called the .50-70 because of its half-inch diameter and seventy-grain powder charge, was used in the Model 1866 Allin conversion, to be dropped in 1873, as a newer cartridge was adopted for service issue.

The new round, the last United States black powder military rifle cartridge, was made in caliber .45, and used seventy grains of powder and a four hundred and five grain lead bullet whose weight was later upped to five hundred grains in order to better burn the powder load by increasing the resistance against which it had to work.

Much of the credit for the success of the metallic cartridge must go to Colonel Hiram Berdan, the famous marksman of Civil War fame. While it is apparent that a metal cartridge was badly needed in all firearms, it is equally apparent that the cartridge, in order to be successful, had to simplify the breech-loading problem, not complicate it. Had rifle primers been unreliable or too difficult or expensive to manufacture, the whole idea might have been abandoned in favor of something else, or at least delayed. Or had the brass cartridge case been unable to live up to the requirements imposed on it, it too would have been a failure. It could easily have happened. For a cartridge is not simple; let us consider some of the design requirements. The cartridge case, which holds all the components together, must be corrosion resistant and sealed so that moisture cannot affect any of the chemicals within it. It must be strong enough to function properly after continued rough treatment. In addition to holding the primer, the head of the case must also serve to seal off the breech against gas leakage. Few rifle actions completely enclose the cartridge; it must while unsupported resist the astronomic pressure within it, and its extracting groove must be hard enough to hold together while the swollen case is being extracted from the chamber. The primer itself develops high pressure and only the presence of the firing pin bearing against it and its own tough construction prevents it from blowing out of the rear of the case and allowing gas to leak into the rifle action. Thus the cartridge case must be thick and tough at the base, where it must resist pressure and the rough treatment of extraction, and thin and springy along most of its length, where it must expand against the chamber walls to perform its function of obturation—all this is required from the same piece of metal.

The cartridge case, besides fulfilling these contradictory requirements, must be inexpensive to make while maintaining high standards of uniformity, for the case must fit accurately and well into any rifle for which it is chambered. The expense and difficulty of turning such items out by the millions by lathework or some similar process is prohibitive; each cartridge case is drawn from a single piece of brass, a process credited to Colonel Berdan.

The case is made from a circular disc of brass which is forced into the shape of a cup and drawn through a series of dies into its final form. The closed end of the drawn tube is pressed into the shape of the cartridge head containing the primer pocket and vent. After all the drawing operations, the case is annealed to remove the strains formed during the manufacturing process. It is a tricky job, after which the base must be hard and tough and the walls must be resilient enough to spring back into shape after firing.

The primer is then pressed into the primer pocket, crimped into position and sealed with a bit of colored lacquer. The case is next filled with a measured amount of propellant and the bullet is seated in the neck of the case to its proper depth.

There are two types of military rifle primers in general use, the Boxer primer and the Berdan primer. The Berdan type, invented by Colonel Berdan, is an almost invariable feature of most foreign rifle cartridges, while the United States favors the Boxer primer. The latter type is made completely separate from the cartridge and is inserted into it as a self-contained unit. It consists of a primer cup which contains the priming compound and an anvil. When the cup is struck by the firing pin, the cup is dented, crushing the compound between cup and anvil. It explodes, flashing a jet of flame through grooves in the anvil and through a vent in the primer pocket into the cartridge case. The Berdan primer is quite similar, except that the anvil is formed from part of the cartridge case itself rather than as part of the primer. The case is pierced by two vents, one on either side of the anvil, and serve the same purpose as those in the Boxer primer. The two primers work equally well; the United States services stick to the Boxer type because it is easier to make. It is constructed separately, and its functioning does not hinge on an accurate fit between the primer cap and the cartridge case. In addition, the Boxer primer cartridge is infinitely easier to reload.

With the invention of the center-fire primer the black powder cartridge had reached its zenith. Its greatest limitation was the propellant itself— black powder. This explosive was simply incapable of producing high velocities without producing more problems than it solved. In its best form, it used a heavy large caliber bullet to achieve with weight what it could not produce with velocity. The bullet struck the target a terrific wallop, but at the cost of high trajectory and the resultant guesswork in hitting targets at unknown ranges. Firing was also accompanied by dense clouds of smoke and the deposition of a thick greasy residue in the bore and action of any weapon in which it was employed. It remained for the invention of smokeless powder in 1886, to usher in a new era in cartridge design.

Conversions to the Cartridge System

THE testing ground provided by the Civil War proved the immeasurable superiority of cartridge arms over the muzzle-loaders. During the length of that war, development proceeded at an accelerated rate, as it always does in wartime, and by 1865 there were some fine cartridge weapons being used by the Army, any one of which would have been a good choice for a new standard shoulder arm. Unfortunately, there were too few of them. The bulk of the Union Army had been armed with rifle muskets, now reduced to little better than relics by the ascendency of magazine cartridge arms. It was high time to modernize our firearms and the Army knew it.

But the war, a big one even by today's dreadful standards, had been won and paid for at sickening cost—thousands dead or crippled, millions of dollars spent, wasted countryside, and half the nation a sullen hostile group of states, to be occupied like conquered foreign territory. And we treated the end of that war as we have treated every one before or since, by regarding it as the last one we would ever have to fight, ever. There was a general and understandable rush to get out of the service, and the Army, emptied of personnel within a few months, collapsed like a punctured tire. No one wanted any part or mention of warfare. There was the country to rebuild and the colossal expanse of western frontier to be opened up. Congress and the people as a whole undoubtedly thought of funds for military research and development as among the last things to be considered. On the military side of the picture, there was cause for worry. The Monroe Doctrine had been openly violated while the United States was fighting for its life in the Civil War; a Hapsburg Prince was Emperor of Mexico, and the strings which governed his actions were pulled by fingers in France. The Army, whose only valid reason for peacetime existence is readiness for combat, had to adopt the attitude that we might have a first class war with France just by asking for it. Circumstances being what they were, the Army made the best of a bad situation by converting its muzzle-loaders, of which it had hundreds of thousands, into single shot cartridge breech-loaders. There were many systems used, but the main conversion design, and eventually the most successful, was that conceived by E. S. Allin, the master armorer of Springfield Armory.

The Allin conversion, Model 1865, left intact the barrel, lock, stock, and metal fittings of the Model 1861 and 1863 rifle muskets. A rectangular hole was milled in the top of the breech end of each barrel, and into the empty space was lowered a breech block, hinged at its forward end, which could be raised by releasing a thumb latch to expose the chamber for loading, and extraction and ejection of the empty case. A firing pin, seated in a hole drilled through the length of the breech block, fired the cartridge upon being struck by the side hammer of the original lock. The act of lifting the breech block after each round was fired actuated a rachet type extractor on the right side of the breech block. The extractor was delicate, unreliable, and was the weakest point of the whole conversion. The latch was also bad, and since neither it nor the firing pin were provided with springs, the whole action rattled rather loosely inside the rifle. In fact the whole original design was extremely poor, and it took years of work to bring it up to the level of a decent rifle.

The bullet diameter remained at caliber .58, the same as the rifle musket, but was housed in a short copper cartridge case, the Martin rimfire cartridge, the first all metal round to be used by the entire United States Army.

Allin Conversion, Model 1866

THE Model 1866 breech-loader was not so much a new rifle as an improved version of the old. The Model 1865 had been a stopgap weapon, admittedly so. After it had been on trial for about a year it underwent several modifications, among them the reduction of caliber to make use of a new center-fire cartridge. Rather than make new barrels, ordnance settled the matter by boring out the original barrels to caliber .64 and brazing a caliber .50, rifled-liner, inside the barrels. The weak rachet extractor of the Model 1865 was replaced by one made from a heavy U-shaped spring. In this design, one arm of the spring engages the rim of the cartridge as it is loaded into the chamber. It is compressed by closing the breech block and expands, when the breech block is lifted, with sufficient force to eject the empty case.

The conversion was made, not only to repair the mistakes made in the design of the Model 1865, but also to allow the use of a center-fire cartridge, the first such venture the Army had tried, and a move that was in advance of most civilian arms. The cartridge did not resemble today's center-fire brass cased round. The Model 1866 cartridge was the folded head or inside primer type, a copper cartridge case with a rim exactly like that of the rimfire round. But the primer was inside the case instead of under the circumference of the rim. The primer was as large as the inside diameter of the cartridge case, and was held in place by two indentations in the side of the case, forming the last evolutionary step prior to the adoption of the conventional center-fire cartridge. Its caliber .50 bullet was a heavy manstopper, a four hundred and fifty grain lead slug propelled by seventy grains of black powder. While certainly an improvement over the rimfire round, it was soon to be replaced by a cartridge whose primer was seated in its base from the outside, a cartridge which could be reloaded after firing, and essentially the same metal round we know today.

The longer cartridge of the Model 1866 necessitated a longer breech block, which was hinged to a plate of metal screwed to the top of the barrel.

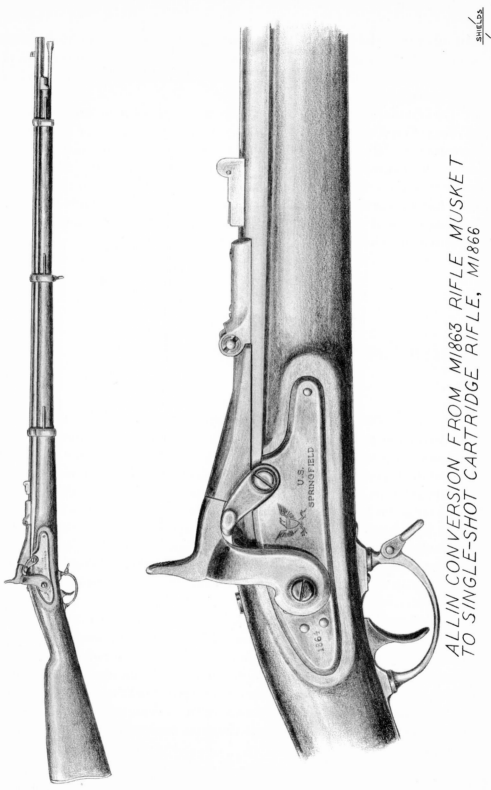

ALLIN CONVERSION FROM M1863 RIFLE MUSKET
TO SINGLE-SHOT CARTRIDGE RIFLE, M1866

But other than the internal changes, both the Model 1865 and Model 1866 were much the same weapon, which in turn, could make the dimensions of either one correspond to those of the Model 1861 of the Model 1863 or any of their variations.

In addition to the Allin system of alterations, there were literally dozens of ideas offered to the Army for testing. Few of them ever got beyond the inventor's model stage. However, several methods of conversion were accepted for limited manufacture. No attempt is made here to even include every type put into production; by and large, their use was too limited and their history was too short. Included are several of what are fairly representational types of what could be done in changing the rifle musket into a cartridge breech-loader.

Joslyn Conversion

ONE of the simplest systems of conversion was the Joslyn, product of the Joslyn Firearms Company of Stonington, Connecticut. In this conversion, the rear end of the barrel was sawed off several inches in front of the barrel tang. To it was attached a cylindrical breech block which was hinged at its left side and could be swung up and to the left to expose the chamber for loading. The firing pin, seated in a hole through the length of the breech block, was operated by a reshaped side hammer which was bent well over the stock in order to reach the firing pin. The original lock mechanism, stock, and furniture were all retained without alteration, though the lock plate was reshaped to fit the action. The Joslyn rifle chambered a caliber .56 rimfire cartridge.

The breech block was stamped B. F. Joslyn's Patent, Oct. 8, 1861, June 24, 1862. The lock plate and other original parts of the rifle would, of course, have the appropriate Springfield Armory or private contractor stampings. Later model Joslyn rifles were improved by the addition of a healthier locking system and a cylindrical shield which protected the rear of the firing pin, and many such weapons were manufactured from scratch at the Joslyn plant. The identifying markings are the same except that the lock plate is

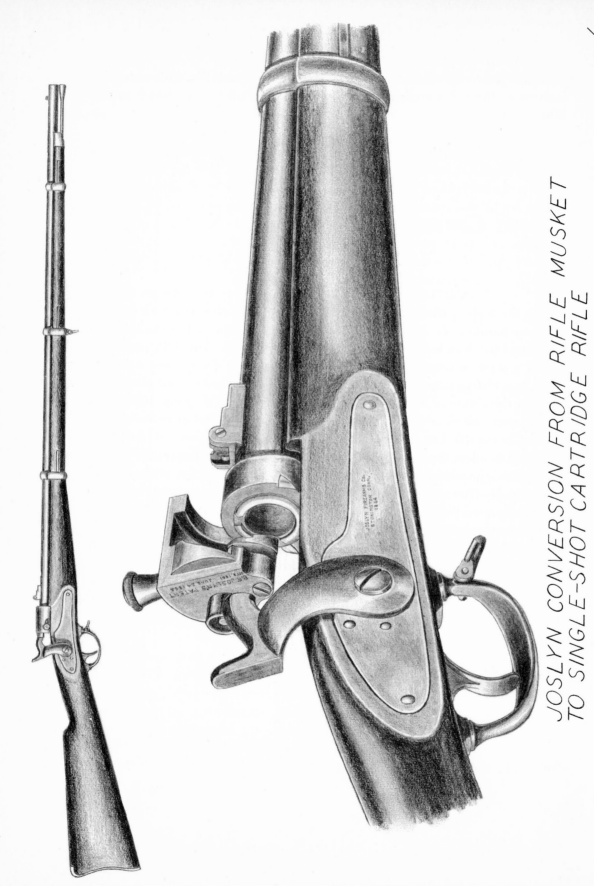

JOSLYN CONVERSION FROM RIFLE MUSKET
TO SINGLE-SHOT CARTRIDGE RIFLE

stamped Joslyn Firearms Co., Stonington, Conn. and the date of manufacture in three horizontal lines. One of these rifles is pictured in the
illustration.

Sharps Conversion

ANOTHER successful conversion was the Sharps system;
unlike the Joslyn, the Sharps could make no use of the weapon's original
lock mechanism. To effect the conversion, the section of the stock which
contained the lockwork was sawed off and discarded. This left, mainly, a
barrel, a stock in two pieces, and the metal furniture. Everything was then
fitted to a Sharps rifle action which had in itself undergone some alteration.
To alter the action to the cartridge system, the Sharps Company substituted
a new breech block which contained a firing pin, and added an extractor and
a hammer modified so as to strike a firing pin. The short breech block was
too small to allow the use of a long straight pin, and the compromise design
resulted in a peculiar U-shaped firing pin which literally had to strike around
a corner. It often struck the primer a weak blow and the twisting to which
it was subjected would usually break it after repeated firing.

These weaknesses notwithstanding, the Sharps rifle action was as tough
as a bone, and it was one of the most popular of the frontier rifles, though
never used in any great quantity by the Army.

U.S. Rifle, Model 1868

EARLY in 1868, the Army definitely decided to retain the
Allin trap door action as the standard breech mechanism for shoulder arms,

and the armory began to turn out the new model weapon, known as the Model 1868. The chief difference between the Model 1868 and its predecessor, the Model 1866, was that the new rifle was made entirely from scratch. The Model 1866 was a conversion from one system to another, employing the old Civil War barrel with a rifled liner inside it, and had no receiver, as such. The breech block was simply inserted into a hole milled in the rear end of the barrel. The Model 1868 was made with a barrel bored out to caliber .50 from a solid steel blank, and the receiver was made as a separate unit. The barrel was screwed into the threaded hole in the receiver ring and the front end of the breech block was hinged to the receiver. The operating principles were exactly the same. The side hammer was thumbed back manually, and the breech block was released by flipping up a thumb latch which was mounted at the rear of the breech block so that the falling hammer covered it and held it securely in place. Once unlatched, the breech block was tilted up and forward; this movement operated the extractor and kicked out the empty cartridge case. A new round was inserted into the chamber and the breech block was closed back behind it, readying the arm for another shot.

The Model 1868 rifle was a caliber .50 single shot breech-loader 52 inches in length and weighed about nine and a quarter pounds. The lock plate, 5.38 inches long and 1.25 inches wide, was flat, bevel-edged, and was inletted into the stock to bevel height. It was marked with a spread eagle, the letters U.S., and the word Springfield in two horizontal lines in front of the hammer. The side hammer was flat and bevel-edged, quite similar to that of the Civil War models; in fact, some of the early Model 1868's utilized Civil War model lock plates.

The 36-inch-round barrel was rifled with three grooves which made one turn in 42 inches. To it were affixed a blade front sight and a sliding leaf rear sight capable of adjustment for long range fire. Two oval bands, anchored by band springs, secured the barrel to the stock, which was tipped with an iron fore end cap. The upper sling swivel was mounted on the upper band, near the muzzle of the rifle. The lower swivel was riveted to the front of the trigger guard. All metal parts were finished by polishing instead of chemical treatment.

All in all, quite similar to the conversion it replaced, with several important visual differences. The Model 1868 had a receiver made as a separate forging, as opposed to the Model 1866 which had no receiver at all. The Model 1868 barrel and stock were held together by two metal bands instead of three. These two differences will alone easily serve to distinguish between one rifle and the other, but there are several others. The small two-leaf rear sight of the Model 1866 was replaced by a sliding leaf sight secured to the barrel by a dovetail mortise and a screw, and the barrel of the Model 1868 has no liner.

U.S. Rifle, Model 1870

SOMETIME after 1868 the receiver of the Model 1868 was redesigned and shortened somewhat, producing a slight overall change in the length of the rifle. The new shortened rifle was known as the Model 1870. Outside of the change in length, which amounted only to .25 inch, and a silver-plated front sight blade, there were only extremely negligible differences between the two rifles. Both the Model 1868 and the Model 1870 rifles fired the same cartridge, a caliber .50 metallic case which was loaded with seventy grains of black powder and a four hundred and fifty grain lead bullet. The round was commonly called the .50-70, after its caliber and powder charge. The Model 1870 rifle was slated to give way, some three years later, to a caliber .45 breech-loader which marked another step in the path towards reduction of caliber in military rifles.

U.S. Rifle, Model 1871 (Remington)

IN 1871, the Army accepted the Remington rifle, which was already in production at Springfield Armory as a Navy rifle, as a good bet for an infantry weapon. The fabrication of ten thousand of them was begun in that year, the Remington company receiving a royalty on each rifle produced. It was a single shot cartridge arm, but a good one, having been in

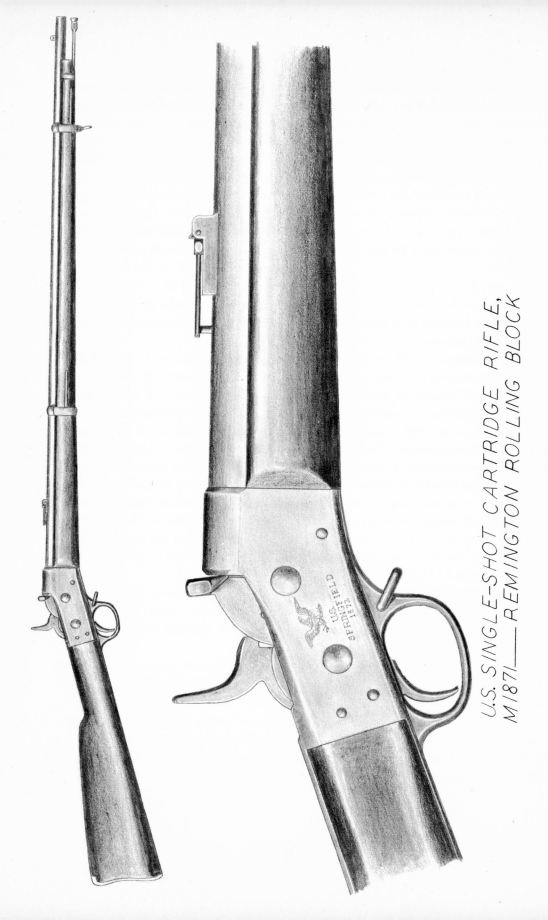

U.S. SINGLE-SHOT CARTRIDGE RIFLE,
M1871 — REMINGTON ROLLING BLOCK

large scale production, in designs of ever-increasing efficiency, since the latter part of the Civil War. The breech action was the internationally known Remington-Rider action, today commonly called the rolling block action. It was simplicity itself. Behind the breech end of the barrel were two moving parts, a hammer and a breech block, both of which were free to rotate about heavy transverse pins driven through the receiver of the rifle. To load the rifle, one thumbed back the hammer to full cock and swung the breech block backwards, exposing the chamber of the barrel. The same motion operated the extractor and moved the hammer forward to half cock. A cartridge was shoved straight into the chamber and the breech block was flipped up behind it in the same motion. Locking was completed as the hammer fell, the two heavy parts forming, in effect, one solid mass of steel behind the cartridge. The breech block, which had a thumbpiece to make its operation simpler, was pierced by a firing pin which transmitted the hammer blow to the cartridge primer.

The Remington rifle, which had its first taste of success in the Civil War, was marketed by a firm which for some years made nothing but money selling it to all comers in Europe. Had there been a general war in Europe in the early 1870's, it would have been fought mostly with Remington rifles. Europe in the late 1860's, with its usual chronic fear of impending war, had neither the know-how nor the facilities to produce really good military rifles, and was a natural market for any firm with a good rifle and a hot sales force. The end of the Civil War drove the Remington company to Europe in search of just such a market, and their rifle was such an astounding success that their faith in its ultimate perfection eventually bankrupted them. But before the magazine rifle eclipsed the single shot arm, Remington rifles were the service arms for Sweden, Denmark, Spain, Egypt, and were sold in tremendous quantity to both France and Prussia.

The original Remington cartridge rifle had a split breech, that is, the hammer fell into a slot in the breech block. It was soon altered by Joseph Rider into its rolling block form, and in this, its final state of development, was accepted by the Army.

The military Remington was a caliber .50 center-fire single shot rifle, 51.75 inches long. The heavy flat receiver, which held the breech block and hammer, separated the stock into two pieces. It was stamped on the right side with U.S. Springfield, the date, and a spread eagle. The left side was marked Model 1871, and the receiver tang was marked with a description of the Remington patents, Remington's Patent. Pat. May 3rd, Nov. 15th, 1864, April 17th, 1868. Into the receiver ring was threaded a 35.75-inch-round barrel, rifled with three broad shallow grooves which twisted uniformly to the right. The forestock was held to the barrel by two oval steel bands, the upper of which was set into the front edge of the trigger guard.

The sighting equipment consisted of a front blade and a ladder-type leaf sight, adjustable up to 1,000 yards, was screwed into the barrel several inches in front of the breech. The normal method of finishing was bright polishing of every metal part except the case hardened receiver.

U.S. Rifle, Model 1873

IN JUNE, 1872, an Ordnance board, presided over by Brigadier General A. H. Terry, was convened for the purpose of testing and adopting a new breech-loading rifle for service issue. It was big doings; ninety-nine domestic rifles and nine foreign ones were included in the tests. Included among the domestic products were well-known designs which were among the probable winners, Remington, Sharps, Ward-Burton, Peabody, Evans, Winchester, and the Springfield in many variations. The foreign rifles tested were the Chassepot, Needle Gun, improved Needle Gun, Needle Carbine, Mauser, Werndl, Werder, Vetterli, and Martini-Henry.

Each rifle was subjected to seven tests; the first was firing with defective cartridges, cases cut and notched so that they would rupture in any of a number of ways. The second consisted of combining rapidity with accuracy, accuracy being a target 6 feet by 2 feet set 100 feet away from the rifle. Each rifle was allowed to fire for one minute. The third was a test for rapidity of unaimed fire, each gun to be fired as rapidly as possible for one minute. Next came an endurance test of five hundred rounds without cleaning. The fifth was the dust test. Each rifle was placed in a special box and exposed to a blast of sand and dust for two minutes. It was removed from the box and fired twenty times, then replaced for two more minutes and fired an additional twenty times. Sixth on the list was the rust test, a brutal one. The chamber of each rifle was plugged with grease and all grease was removed from every other portion of the breech mechanism. The gun was dipped butt first in a solution of sal-amoniac and held there to the level of its

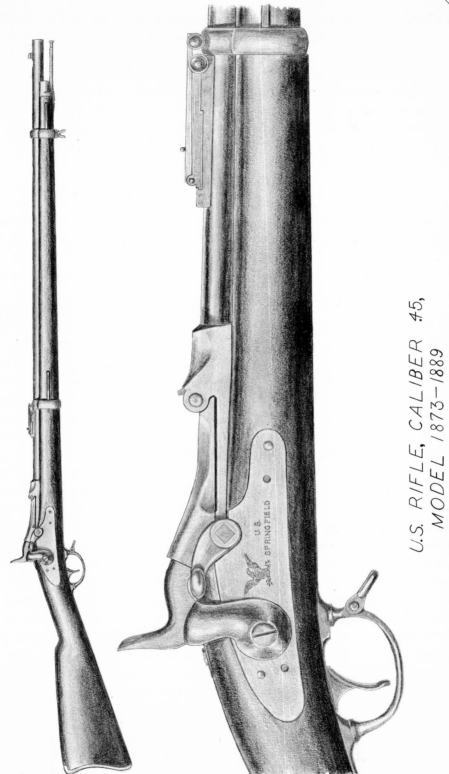

SHIELDS

U.S. RIFLE, CALIBER .45,
MODEL 1873-1889

U.S.
MODEL 1873. SPRINGFIELD

chamber for ten minutes. Afterwards, it was exposed to air for two days and fired twenty times. The last test was firing with excessive loads; the rifles were fired with eighty-five grains of powder and one four hundred and fifty grain bullet. It was fired again with ninety grains of powder and one bullet, and finally with ninety grains and two bullets.

After preliminary testing, twenty-one domestic rifles were retained for further tests, among them the Sharps, Remington, Springfield, Winchester, Whitney, and a group of lesser lights. Two foreign rifles out of the nine made it, the Werndl and the Martini-Henry.

In addition to the marathon-style testing, various rifles were submitted and issued out to infantry, cavalry, and artillery units for use in the field. Most of these were either Springfield, Sharps, Remington, and Ward-Burton, the only bolt action rifle in the lot. The Springfield Allin action seems to have won hands down in matters of freedom from misfires, breakage of parts, extraction difficulties, and in preference by the officers commanding the companies in which the rifles were used.

After all the results were in, the board decided to retain the trapdoor action Springfield design, an outgrowth of the original Allin conversion of 1865. In a sense it is not difficult to see why the Allin action was adopted for use at that time. The rifle was simple in the extreme, reliable, easy to manufacture, and fired a bullet with a formidable impact. But the Army seemed to be a little uneasy about its choice, as well it might. Subsequent experiments hinged about detachable magazines whose use was supposed to increase the Springfield's rate of fire. Most of these magazines were solid blocks of wood drilled with a series of holes a little larger than the diameter of the cartridges and roughly half their length. Cartridges were stuck bullet first into the blocks, which were attached to the rifle stocks, and were removed one at a time and shoved into the chamber for firing. On a target range their use permitted rapid fire, but under field conditions the arrangement was hopeless, producing a system far inferior to the magazine rifles which had been turned down. The Army's viewpoint may be summed up in the words of its own testing board, "Resolved, that in the opinion of the Board, the adoption of magazine-guns for the military service, by all nations, is only a question of time; that whenever an arm shall be devised which shall be as effective as a single breech-loader, as the best of the existing arms, and at the same time shall possess a safe and easily manipulated magazine, every consideration of public policy will require its adoption." Thus, with heavy military circumlocution, the Army expressed a desire for a rifle better than the one it had. Perhaps that better rifle was already in existence, but

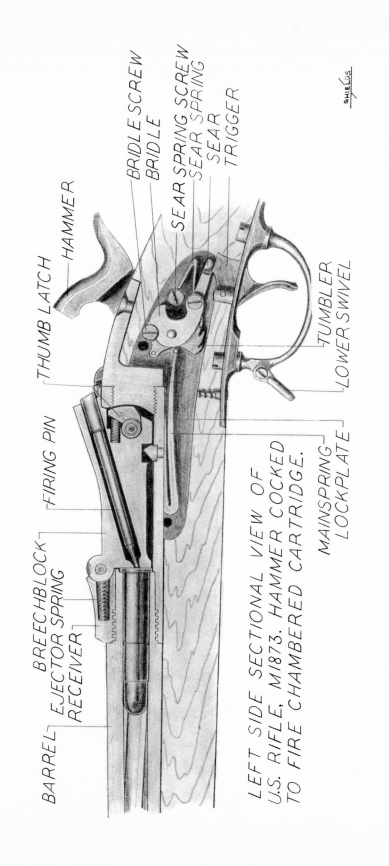

SHIELDS

HAMMER

BRIDLE SCREW
BRIDLE

SEAR SPRING SCREW
SEAR SPRING
SEAR
TRIGGER

THUMB LATCH

TUMBLER
LOWER SWIVEL

FIRING PIN

MAINSPRING
LOCKPLATE

BARREL
BREECHBLOCK
EJECTOR SPRING
RECEIVER

LEFT SIDE SECTIONAL VIEW OF
U.S. RIFLE, M1873. HAMMER COCKED
TO FIRE CHAMBERED CARTRIDGE.

had failed to operate properly after sitting around in a pail of ammonia. In that same year, 1873, civilians, who weren't so particular, began buying up Winchester '73's, a caliber .44 lever action magazine rifle. So did the Indians. In addition to the serious and sincere testing done by the Army Board, other military voices were raised against the magazine rifle. One little gem of criticism, often used, stated that the shifting of weight as a tubular magazine was emptied would affect the balance of the rifle and interfere with accurate firing. Really. With so much eloquence raised against it, it was small wonder that the repeating rifle was not adopted. The single shot arm which was accepted was manufactured, with only minor variations, until 1892, and indeed many of our troops were armed with it when the Army landed in Cuba in 1898. The Model 1873 figured prominently in another fiasco, as the weapon with which Custer's troops were armed when they were wiped out at the Little Big Horn.

The same tests which resulted in the Model 1873 rifle also brought about the reduction of caliber from .50 to .45. This new ammunition was originally loaded with seventy grains of powder and a four hundred and five grain bullet for the rifle and a carbine load powered by fifty-five grains of powder. During the early 1880's the bullet weight was increased to five hundred grains. Though by now an old cartridge, the .45-70 is still a splendid effective load for hunting, especially in close timber or at short range, where the massive slug can inflict damage before it has a chance to drop too far or lose too much velocity. Commercial rifle manufacturers were quick to take note of it, and the Model 1886 Winchester and several later rifles were chambered for this potent round.

The rifle was a single shot breech-loader, caliber .45, with a total length of 52 inches. In general appearance it differed little from the percussion weapons from which it descended. The lock plate, 5.38 inches long and 1.31 inches wide, was completely flat and was set flush with the surface of the stock. It was marked with the letters U.S. surmounting the word Springfield, both stamped in horizontal lines. Between the lettering and the hammer was a spread eagle facing towards the front of the lock plate. The hammer, with a large cocking spur, was convexly rounded on the outer surface.

The 33-inch-round barrel, our first to be made of steel instead of iron, was rifled with three grooves which made one turn in 22 inches. It was marked with an eagle's head, arrows, and the letters U.S. It was held to the stock by two oval steel bands, each of which was retained by band springs forward of each band.

The walnut stock, 48.8 inches long, was tipped with a steel fore end cap;

behind the lock plate it was straight with a slight comb and a deep crescent curve at the butt plate.

Aside from the reduction of caliber from .50 to .45 and the employment of stronger materials, it was quite similar to the Models 1868 and 1870. There were, however, a number of definite visual differences which easily serve to differentiate between the Model 1873 and its forerunners. As previously mentioned, the lock plate was set flush into the stock instead of being beveled; the hammer was rounded, whereas the two previous models employed flat bevel-edged hammers. The lower sling swivel was screwed to the trigger guard instead of riveted to it, and every metal part was chemically blued.

U.S. Rifle, Models 1879, 1884, and 1889

WORK on the Model 1873 never really stopped. Over the years the rifle was made with a whole host of minor improvements, few of them visible to the eye and none of them of sufficient magnitude to warrant calling the finished product a new model. Such changes as a slight increase in the height of the stock comb, case hardening of parts, and the issue of various experimental bayonets went on intermittently after 1873. As weapons were hauled in for repair they were improved to the extent of these new alterations, to bring them up to the level of the new rifles, until the Model 1873's which survive to this day have a bewildering array of minor differences; an issue weapon with different dates on the barrel, breech block, and receiver, topped with either an early or late model rear sight is not at all uncommon.

In 1879 it was believed that a sufficient number of changes had occurred to call the product by a new model number. This model, called the Model 1879, had a trap in the butt plate and rear sights of the buckhorn type, well known to hunters, were added to the rifle. Otherwise it was the same as the Model 1873, plus or minus whatever minor changes it might or might not have.

After 1879, the rifle came out in two experimental forms, a short rifle version, and a rifle equipped with a sliding rod bayonet permanently attached to the rifle, neither of which saw extended manufacture or issue. In 1884, the rifle came out of the arsenals with still another rear sight, the invention of Colonel Buffington. This sight was very elaborate and had provisions for making adjustments in elevation, windage, and automatic correction for drift, and is perhaps the best known sight on the .45-70 rifle. When the rifle was fired at extended ranges, the sight leaf was placed in a vertical position, a knurled knob allowing the slide to be held at any desired range setting. This slide was mounted in a pair of tracks which forced it progressively further to the left as the elevation was increased, offsetting the drift caused by the right hand twist of the rifling. It was at this time that the bullet weight of the ammunition was increased to five hundred grains over the original four hundred and five grains. These rifles, otherwise the same as the older ones, were stamped on the breech block U. S. Model 1884.

In 1889, another model appeared, the same as the Model 1884, with the exception of a newly designed rod bayonet and a trigger guard made in one piece, whose lower sling swivel was secured to the guard by riveting instead of the usual machine screw.

This model turned out to be our last single shot rifle. It marked the complete extension of the heavy caliber, single shot, and black powder combination which had been in use since the beginning of firearms. Though the trend was towards magazine rifles the Army stuck stubbornly by it, considering it to be the best possible military shoulder arm. In a lecture given to the United States Artillery School at Fort Monroe, Virginia, one Lieutenant Charles A. Bennett voiced the military opinion on firearms of the late 1880's. In an odd mixture of blindness and prophecy, Lt. Bennett summed up his views on future development, "The future development of guns is a puzzle. Within forty years we changed from the flintlock to a gun that has fired as many as fifty shots a minute. It is easy to see how the rapidity of fire can be increased. A soldier could carry all his cartridges in a magazine, slung over his shoulder and by inserting the end of it in his gun, might shoot his entire supply of cartridges in a couple of minutes.

"But this is not what is wanted; the soldier who can shoot so rapidly wastes his ammunition and is soon out of cartridges.

"If an effort is required between each discharge, that of loading, he will be more careful with his cartridges, and can be better controlled in his fire, by officers. Some have even objected to magazine guns on this ground. A soldier can carry but a limited supply of ammunition. In the present guns he has always a few in reserve in his magazine. It is thus hard to see how this gun, as a military arm, can be improved, even by increasing its rapidity of fire, since this desirable feature almost certainly entails waste of ammunition.

"If rapidity of fire will not make a better military gun, in what manner will it be improved? Certainly not much in range and accuracy. Explosive bullets are forbidden by most civilized nations. Some other explosive than gunpowder may solve the problem."

It doesn't pay to be smug about anything in the realm of physical sciences. Two years prior to this lecture, in 1884, a Frenchman named Vieille pulled a sneaky trick by inventing that entirely new propellant, boosting firearms, almost overnight, to roughly the level they occupy today. Range and accuracy have improved, and always will. Rapidity of fire and waste of ammunition? What nation today would be caught without a large stock of machine guns and automatic cannon? The one-shot-at-a-time advocates simply overlooked the fact that as ammunition expenditure is increased, so supply facilities are increased. A large portion of rapid fire is undoubtedly wasted, that is, it fails to connect with some given target; but if one nation adopts rapid-fire weapons, all must adopt rapid-fire weapons, in order to stay even.

Magazine Rifles

BREECH-LOADING and repeating firearms are far from new. In fact, the necessity for rapid fire must have appeared concurrently with the invention of the first successful firearms, which were in reality far inferior to the bow and arrow they challenged. In the Artillery Museum in Paris is a breech-loader made in 1550 and also a matchlock revolver of about the same era, the age of which attests to the great antiquity of the problem. The advantages of a repeating arm are manifest. The easiest way of producing rapid fire from the early guns was to keep adding barrels to them, as was done with ancient artillery, but the deadly increase in weight precluded their use in firearms meant to be carried rather than towed. Early portable firearms were so slow to reload that the only way to gain rapidity of fire was to carry around several of them. Mounted troops carried two pistols slung from the pommel of the saddle. Old illustrations of pirates and Navy privateers invariably show them with a large baldric slung over one shoulder, with a number of single shot flintlock pistols depending from it, for after having fired its one round, the gun was good only as a crude club. Foot soldiers, having neither horses nor ships to carry around the weight of their equipment, relied on easily reloadable smoothbore weapons, bayonet, and volley fire to protect themselves. Though some repeating weapons were made over the centuries, some ingenious, some incredibly impractical, the single shot weapon was the only firearm dependable, simple, and cheap enough to make the grade in military service. This was a compound trouble, for soldiers in combat needed rapid fire more than any other group of men who handled firearms. A defending force could be overwhelmed by a charge made in successive waves, the second wave overrunning the positions while the defenders, who had expended their ammunition on the first group of attackers, were frantically trying to reload. Some odd tactics evolved out of this difficulty. The British hollow square was a famous example. It was a literal hollow square of three ranks of men, the first of which lay prone, the second knelt, and the third fired from the standing position. Any rank could deliver a closely packed volley and reload while the enemy charge was under engagement by fire from either of the other ranks. A splendid defense system and an equally splendid target—one cluster of men standing shoulder to shoulder and three deep. The square was a specialized formation used by men who were greatly outnumbered and surrounded, but the principles it employed to gain fire power were the general principles of the tactics then in use. Remedial steps were not too successful. One could reduce the density of the target formed by several ranks of troops by stringing the men out in a long thin scattered line, but the limited range and rate of fire of the weapon in use would also reduce the density of fire and the ease and certainty of control. A fair proportion of the attacking force was bound to get through. Partly as a result of this contradiction, infantry formations remained close-packed masses of men who were effective only if the enemy chose to fight in the same manner.

The difficulty was overcome in the handgun field some years before the invention of the metallic cartridge, with the invention of the Colt revolver. The Mexican War showed it to be an astonishing success. A group of men armed with revolvers could put out six times the volume of fire ordinarily expected to come from them. But rifles, with their heavier calibers and powder charges, needed a sturdier system. The prayer was answered by the appearance of the metallic cartridge which in short order made magazine rifles possible.

Two magazine rifles were designed in time for a tryout in the Civil War, the Henry and the Spencer. The Henry was destined to become the Winchester, and achieve a position of great permanence, as far as firearms go; the Spencer was bought up by Winchester after the Civil War, in order to eliminate competition.

Henry Magazine Rifle, Model 1860

THE first magazine rifle to see anything like widespread service in the United States Army was the Henry rifle, the invention of B. Tyler Henry, a caliber .44 lever action repeater which was the first such rifle issued in the Civil War. Though few in number, the Henrys became known for their brutal efficiency on Sherman's march to the sea, as the principal armament of two infantry regiments under Major General Dodge. Just where earlier weapons stopped and where the Henry rifle began is hard to say. Henry seems to have been a machinist with the manufacturers of the Jennings rifle, a magazine shoulder arm of 1849 vintage. It was in itself an improvement over an earlier weapon, Walter Hunt's Volition Repeater. This was a few years before the invention of the metallic cartridge and the Jennings rifle employed a Rube Goldberg cartridge consisting of a deeply hollow bullet whose base contained a fulminate propellant, covered by a thin wad. Ignition was by external means. Nonetheless, it was a lever action repeating arm, fed by a tubular magazine under the barrel, and except for its side hammer and ring trigger, looked remarkably like rifles of much later design. Patent rights to the Jennings mechanism were obtained by Horace Smith and Daniel Wesson, who manufactured an improved version of it under the name of Volcanic Firearms. By this time the action had acquired a centrally hung hammer and a rising-link carrier block which was worked by the trigger guard lever, and whose purpose was to transfer cartridges from the magazine to the chamber. Smith and Wesson's product was manufactured as a pistol and in limited number as a carbine. Their repeating cartridge handgun looked quite a bit like a conventional lever action rifle would if the barrel were shortened and the stock were cut off and replaced by pistol grips. When Smith and Wesson bought the Rollin White patent which effectively covered revolver cylinders made to handle metallic cartridges, they decided to concentrate on revolvers and sold their patent rights outright to the Volcanic Repeating Arms Company. The Volcanic weapons fired the unpredictable fulminate propelled cartridges which corroded out the barrels through which they were used, and the company went out of business in 1857. It was bought by Oliver Winchester, a New England textile tycoon, who renamed the outfit the New Haven Arms Company and retained B. Tyler Henry as plant superintendent. Henry realized that the improved Volcanic action was a sound one, but would never get anywhere firing the cartridge it did. His first job was that of cartridge design and he chose the same line of approach as did Smith and Wesson with their revolver cartridge, producing a cartridge with a small fulminate primer under the circumference of the rim, and a black powder propelling charge. Patents for the Henry rifle, with its improved rimfire cartridge, were granted in 1860. In honor of Henry's achievement, the Winchester firm stamped the letter H on the head of every rimfire cartridge they manufactured, a practice they follow to this day.

In military form the Henry was a caliber .44 rimfire magazine repeating rifle with a 24-inch octagonal barrel and a total length of 43.5 inches. The six-groove rifling was of a now-unusual type called a gain twist whose purpose was to start the bullet easily into the rifling and then spin it at progressively higher rotational speeds, the highest speed being attained at the muzzle. The rifling began with a twist of one turn in 16 feet and at the muzzle made one turn in 33 inches. The receiver was flat and deep with an exposed hammer behind it, and a hinged lever and trigger guard combination, to which were attached the bolt, locking mechanism and lifting block for moving cartridges from the magazine to the chamber, was hinged to the bottom of the frame. There was no forestock; the tubular magazine, which extended from the front of the frame to the barrel muzzle, served as a handgrip. A wooden buttstock was attached to the rear of the frame. The entire frame, locking mechanism, lever, and butt plate were made of bronze; the remaining metal parts were made of iron. The barrel was stamped with the following, Henry's Patent Oct. 16, 1860, Manufct'd by New Haven Arms Co., New Haven, Ct. A blade front sight was mounted on the barrel near the muzzle and a leaf rear sight was a little forward of the frame.

The rifle's chief weakness lay in the method of loading the tubular magazine. The coil spring, which fed fifteen cartridges from the muzzle end back into the frame, had to be manually compressed up to the muzzle end of the magazine before the tube could be loaded. Not a difficult job, because a metal slide protruded through a slot cut along the entire length of the magazine tube; the slot, however, formed a perfect trap for any foreign matter small enough to fit into it. When the spring was compressed, the cap on the muzzle end of the magazine was swung around, permitting the insertion of the cartridges, base first. The loading arrangement was soon to be changed, but the lock mechanism set a pattern that has lasted to this day. By depressing the lever, one automatically extracted the empty round, cocked the hammer, and put a live cartridge in position for loading into the chamber. The return of the lever to its closed position reloaded the rifle and locked the cartridge in the chamber.

The Henry rimfire cartridge, though dependable, was a fairly weak round. It was a short caliber .44 brass rimfire case loaded with twenty-eight grains of black powder behind a two hundred grain lead bullet. While not much of a load, it was not materially improved until some years after the Civil War.

One thousand seven hundred and thirty-one Henry rifles were purchased for Army issue during the Civil War, a minute fraction of the total number of shoulder arms involved. Before the kinks were ironed out and a magazine rifle of any kind was accepted for standard issue by the Army, a period of thirty-two years was to elapse.

Spencer Magazine Rifle, Model 1865

IN 1860, when the Army was firmly dedicated to the course of employing muzzle-loading single shot rifle muskets, which seemed to be the best weapons in sight, there was patented an amazingly advanced lever action magazine rifle, the invention of Christopher M. Spencer. Its action contained everything the military forces needed—fixed ammunition, tremendous celerity of fire, and detachable, easily-loaded magazines, a formidable combat combination, especially when viewed alongside the rifle

SPENCER REPEATING RIFLE

musket. However, bureaucracy is bureaucracy; in the Civil War, Washington was about what it is now, and Spencer, in attempting to interest the Army in his weapon, was shuttled from office to office, his chances of success being in inverse proportion to the number of people he saw. It was not until someone suggested that he bypass channels and see Lincoln himself that Spencer received an order for his rifle, which was to the muzzle-loader as the saber was to the penknife.

The Military Spencer rifle employed a trigger guard lever which, when lowered, served to open the breech, extract the empty cartridge case, and permit the spring-fed magazine to feed a new cartridge into the chamber. Cocking of the hammer was, like that of the Sharps rifle, independent of any movement of the lever, and it had to be manually thumbed back prior to firing each shot. The magazine was a detachable metal tube which was inserted into the buttstock of the rifle. It operated much like a modern automatic pistol magazine, consisting of a metal body, floor plate, follower spring, and follower. Seven copper case rimfire cartridges were pushed base first against the follower, which compressed the follower spring and furnished power to feed the cartridges one at a time, into the chamber as the lever was lowered. While loading each magazine was fairly slow, it was no slower than loading the magazine of the most modern automatic pistol or the BAR, and anyway, the soldier carried a box containing ten magazines, giving him seventy rounds available for rapid delivery. The Spencer was limited by the power of its cartridge, a short rimfire load of forty-five grains of black powder, and the fact that the copper cases would tend to stick to the chamber walls as the rifle heated up from sustained firing. In range and muzzle energy the Spencer was decidedly inferior to the rifle musket.

The Spencer rifle receiver was a flat sided machining which contained the breech block and a large trigger guard hinged at its forward end about a transverse pin. It was stamped Spencer Repeating Rifle Co., Boston, Mass. Pat'd March 6, 1860. The hammer and trigger and tumbler mechanism were not housed in the receiver, but formed a separate lock mechanism set into the right side of the buttstock. The stock was of the two-piece variety common to lever action rifles, a walnut buttstock, which housed the lock mechanism and the magazine well, and a forestock held to the barrel by three oval steel bands. The middle band held the upper sling swivel and the lower swivel was set into the lower edge of the buttstock.

The 30-inch-round barrel was rifled with three grooves, and carried a blade front sight and a sliding leaf rear sight. All metal parts were glued except for the case hardened receiver.

[121]

Though the original Spencer rifles were manufactured without any magazine cutoff, later specimens were equipped with one invented by Edward M. Stabler. The Stabler cutoff prevented the breech block from being lowered far enough to expose the open end of the magazine, and its use allowed the rifle to be used as a single-loader or as a magazine rifle. Not having the financial backing of the Henry rifle, the Spencer firm went out of business in 1869. When the plant was sold at auction, it was bought by the Winchester Repeating Arms Company, and its design disappeared permanently from the firearms market.

Winchester Magazine Rifle, Model 1866

AT the end of the Civil War the New Haven Arms Company was reorganized and named the Winchester Repeating Arms Company. In 1866, the company acquired King's patent for charging the magazine through a loading gate in the side of the frame, and the new rifle was designated the Winchester Model 1866, the first rifle to bear the Winchester name.

The Winchester Model 1866 was fundamentally the same weapon as the Henry rifle, except that the loading procedure was vastly improved by the addition of the side loading gate, whose use simplified the procedure considerably. The live cartridges were inserted, one at a time, into the breech end of the magazine by pressing them down on the loading gate cover and shoving them forward. The side loading gate also did away with the worst feature of the Henry rifle, an open slot, vulnerable to mud and sand, which extended along the length of the magazine tube.

The early specimens of the Model 1866 rifle had octagonal barrels 24 inches in length and half-length forestocks, but the majority of those issued out were as described below.

The frame of the rifle was a heavy slab-sided affair made of brass which enclosed the entire lock mechanism of the rifle. A 27-inch-round barrel, marked Henry's Pat. Oct. 16, 1860, and King's Pat. March 29, 1866, protruded from the front of the frame. It was bored to caliber .44, rifled with five grooves which twisted to the right. The 23.5-inch tubular magazine,

WINCHESTER REPEATING RIFLE, MODEL 1866

SHIELDS

which lay under the barrel, had a capacity of fifteen cartridges. The stock was in two sections, a buttstock capped by a brass butt plate and a forestock whose length was almost equal to that of the magazine. It was held to the barrel by two oval bands, the upper of which held the upper sling swivel. The lower swivel was on the lower edge of the buttstock. A third metal band encircled both the barrel and the magazine tube near the muzzle of the rifle. All metal parts were blued, with the exception of the brass receiver, lever, and butt plate, which were often nickel-plated. A blade front sight was dovetailed into the barrel near the muzzle, and the rear sight, a vertical sliding leaf type adjustable for elevation, was affixed to the barrel several inches in front of the frame.

The rifle was chambered for a caliber .44 rimfire cartridge loaded with twenty-eight grains of black powder and a two hundred grain lead bullet. The cartridge was fed into the chamber by a bolt which traveled straight to the rear as the trigger guard lever was depressed, and straight forward as the lever was returned to its trigger guard position under the frame. Locking was achieved by a toggle action on either side of the bolt; the toggles folded into a V for unlocking and were straightened out parallel to the bolt when the lever was closed against the underside of the frame.

The cycle of operation might be best understood if we suppose that a cartridge has just been fired and that there are live rounds in the magazine. As the lever is depressed, it pulls the locking toggles into their inoperative V position, and at the same time causes the bolt to be retracted to the rear. The extractor claw, on the top of the bolt, pulls the empty case clear of the chamber. There is a carrier block in a vertical well to the rear of the magazine tube and barrel, operated by a bell crank attached to the lever; and as the lever is depressed it rises straight up in its shaft behind the magazine and chamber. Spring tension on the magazine follower has already forced a live round into the lifting or carrier block. As the block rises, its top kicks the empty case through the open top of the frame, and at the top of its rise the live round occupies the space in front of the bolt. The bolt, meanwhile, has been forced to the rear, rotating the hammer backwards against the pressure of its spring, where it is held by the sear. As the lever is returned to its original position, all the operations are reversed. The bolt moves forward, picking up the new round and ramming it home into the chamber. The carrier block, which rose as the bolt was retracted, now drops straight down as the bolt moves forward. It hits bottom as the lever is closed, and the magazine follower feeds a new round into the carrier block. The hammer, held by the sear, remains in its cocked position until the trigger is pulled. At

[124]

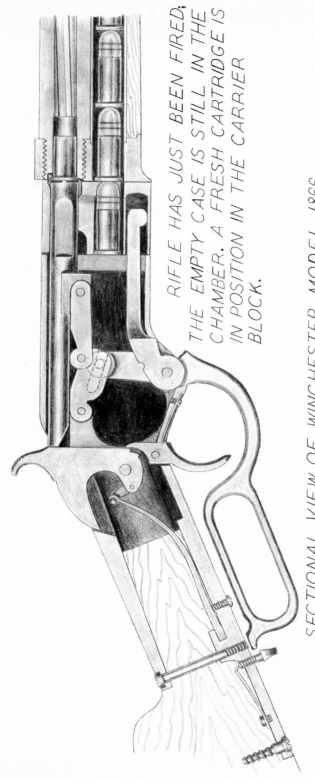

RIFLE HAS JUST BEEN FIRED; THE EMPTY CASE IS STILL IN THE CHAMBER. A FRESH CARTRIDGE IS IN POSITION IN THE CARRIER BLOCK.

SHIELDS

SECTIONAL VIEW OF WINCHESTER MODEL 1866

such time it rotates forward under the power of its compressed spring and strikes the firing pin within the bolt, which in turn transmits the blow to the cartridge primer and fires the round.

For out and out rapidity of fire, there is no beating it, unless by a semi-automatic or full automatic weapon. The lever action rifle had many advantages possessed by no other rifle of its day. Its chamber could be reloaded with extreme rapidity while the rifle was still in firing position against the firer's shoulder and the firer's face was pressed against the stock, something almost impossible with the later-day bolt action rifles, and totally so with the single shot breech-loaders which the Army was then using. In handling the single shot rifle, the shooter had to take the rifle from his shoulder, release his firing grip on it, flip up the breech block, insert a fresh cartridge, close the breech, and lift the rifle up to his shoulder again and resight it. Not so with the lever action rifle, which was reloaded with a sharp downward and upward snap of the right hand and wrist. Even the most modern bolt action rifles are inferior to the lever action in respect to ease, speed, and facility of operation, though today they have far outstripped it in strength, simplicity, and extremes of accuracy. The chief drawback to bolt action speed is that one's grip must be released to grab the bolt handle, work it, and then regrip the rifle.

The Model 1866, used only in small numbers as a military weapon, left room for considerable improvement, especially in its cartridge, the sluggish rimfire load. In 1873, the Winchester Company switched to a center-fire caliber .44 cartridge powered by forty grains of black powder. The brass receiver was replaced by a stronger one made of iron, and the new product was the famous Winchester '73, which played such a rich role in the winning of the West.

However, the '73, whatever its merits or lack of them, was never a military rifle. The company submitted a rifle in the 1873 tests, but failed to sell the Army on anything until 1878, and it wasn't a lever action rifle.

U.S. Magazine Rifle, Model 1878 (Hotchkiss)

THE ARMY was well satisfied with the single-shot Spring-field, and its chief complaint centered about the fact that there weren't enough of them. The civil components of the Government claimed that firearms changed so rapidly that by the time a weapon was in full production it would be obsolete. All the Army had to do was to keep experimenting and produce pilot models for rifles to be made in the event of a war. If such were the case the Army would begin a war with the very latest in firearms. Besides, it would save money.

In the fiscal year ending June 30, 1878, one hundred thousand dollars were appropriated for small arms manufacture. The Army promptly submitted an estimate of nine hundred thousand dollars for the following year. In his annual report to the Secretary of War, General S. V. Benét, then Chief of Ordnance, wrote, with faultless logic, the following, "The moral effect of a large supply of arms in readiness for use is always disregarded in the discussion of the subject. To be prepared for immediate hostilities is a quiet power, which must enter largely as an important factor in the determination of international questions that may or may not lead to war and, as such power, it is worth all the money expended in its production. The argument so frequently used, that the gun of today will probably be superseded by a superior invention of a few years hence, and the expense of today be money thrown away, might be used with equal force and pertinence respecting any article of manufacture whatever."

With finances being the main point of contention, experimentation on and manufacture of new small arms was bound to be limited. The time span between the close of the Civil War and the adoption of the Krag-Jörgensen rifle in 1892, encompassed a period wherein a number of magazine rifles were adopted for extended field trials, but in extremely limited number, a few hundred or so at a time. In 1878 a total of twenty thousand dollars out of the

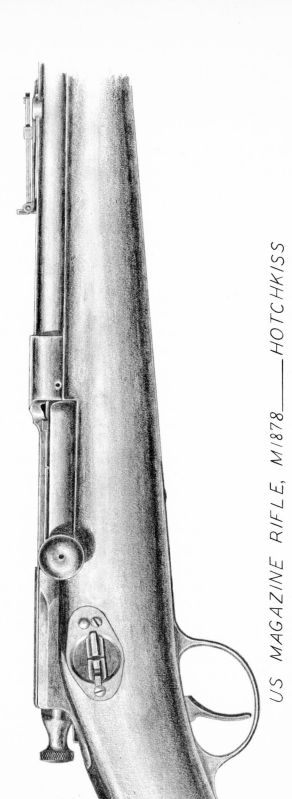

US MAGAZINE RIFLE, M1878 ———— HOTCHKISS

SHIELDS

original appropriation of one hundred thousand dollars was allocated for manufacture of magazine rifles, provided a board of Ordnance officers, appointed by the Secretary of War, recommended such arms for military service.

On April 3, 1878, a board was convened for the purpose of testing and adopting a magazine rifle for the services. The usual notices, announcing the coming tests, were circulated in the newspapers for a little over three months. Twenty-seven various rifles, representing sixteen different makes and designs, were entered into the competition. Some of the rifles haven't been heard of before or since, but most of them were fairly well known, the Hotchkiss, Remington, Sharps, Ward, Ward-Burton, Winchester, and a few lesser lights.

The tests were conducted along much the same lines as those for the Model 1873. The first test was rapidity with accuracy, two minutes of firing at a target 6 feet by 2 feet from a distance of 100 feet; the second was rapidity at will; the third was firing with defective cartridges, followed by the dust and rust tests previously described. The last was firing with excessive charges, one round with eighty-five grains of powder and a four hundred and five grain bullet, one round with ninety grains of powder and a four hundred and five grain bullet, and one round consisting of ninety grains of powder stoppered up by two bullets.

The winner was the Hotchkiss, a bolt action rifle backed by the Winchester company. It was a caliber .45 center-fire rifle, 48.6 inches in length. The 28.6-inch-round barrel was held to the full-length stock by two oval steel bands. The upper sling swivel was mounted on the upper band and the lower swivel was attached to the front of the trigger guard. As on the later model 1873 Springfields, the upper band also carried a stacking swivel. Except for the case hardened receiver, all metal parts were chemically blued. The receiver was stamped with the following, Manufactured by the Winchester Repeating Arms Co., New Haven, Conn., U.S.A. and Pat. Oct. 16, 1860, June 25, 1872, July 23, 1878, and under B. B. Hotchkiss Pats. Aug. 17, 1868, Feb. 15, 1870, Nov. 9, 1875, Nov. 14, 1876, Jan. 23, 1877. The front sight was attached to a lug which doubled as a bayonet stud. A sliding leaf rear sight was dovetailed into the barrel about 4 inches in front of the receiver ring.

The bolt was composed of three parts, a bolt body, bolt head, and a cocking piece, to which the firing pin was secured by a screw thread. The bolt body was hollowed out to receive the firing pin and its spring. The bolt

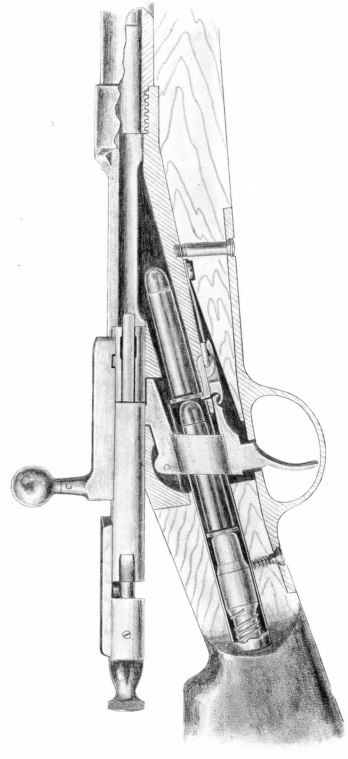

SECTIONAL VIEW OF M1878 HOTCHKISS RIFLE. BOLT IS OPEN AND TOPMOST CARTRIDGE, HAVING PASSED ITS STOP, IS BEING FED INTO THE CHAMBER.

SHIELDS

head, which supported the cartridge at the instant of firing, carried the extractor attached to it by a dovetail tenon.

When the bolt was unlocked by turning it to the left, the cocking piece was cammed back beyond the nose of the sear, or upper extremity of the trigger, withdrawing the tip of the firing pin into the head of the bolt. When the bolt was locked, which was done by turning the handle into a cut in the receiver, the firing pin spring was compressed. By pressing the trigger, the sear was drawn from the cocking piece, and the firing pin, driven forward by its compressed spring, exploded the cartridge.

The magazine was in the buttstock. A hole was drilled in the receiver at its rear end, below the bolt and at an angle to the axis of the barrel. Through this hole the cartridges were fed from the magazine into the receiver, where the bolt forced them into the chamber. The trigger was bent around the magazine tube. A cartridge stop was connected to it, below the tube. When the magazine was filled by pressing cartridges into it from the receiver, the front cartridge pressed against the cartridge stop. By pulling the trigger, the stop was depressed below the level of the magazine, and the first cartridge, under pressure of the magazine spring, slips by and bears against the underside of the bolt. When the bolt is pulled back, the first cartridge is driven up by the spring into the receiver. Pulling the trigger to fire one cartridge permits the next one to partly enter the receiver, the operation being completed when the bolt is withdrawn with the empty shell of the previous round.

A magazine cutoff, located behind the bolt handle on the right side of the stock, allows the use of the rifle as a single-loader, with the full magazine capacity of five rounds held in reserve. The ammunition was of standard service size, the .45-70-405 cartridge originally designed for the Model 1873 Springfield.

Only a few thousand Hotchkiss rifles were manufactured by the Winchester Company under Army contracts before a new group of magazine rifle tests rendered the original Hotchkiss obsolescent.

U.S. Magazine Rifle, Model 1882 (Lee)

IN 1882, General Benét's annual report to the Secretary of War stated that the Springfield single-shot breech-loading arms continued to give such satisfactory service that they would be retained as the standard shoulder arms for the Army until such time as they were replaced by a magazine rifle. And they were still looking for that rifle.

On July 5, 1881, a board had been assembled for some fifteen months of small arms testing, with the understanding that if the board found any rifles suitable for adoption, General Benét was to recommend the manufacture or purchase of a limited number for field tests.

Forty rifles on thirteen systems, some being duplicates or slight modifications of others, were submitted. Winchester submitted an improved Hotchkiss, in competition of such rifles as the Lee, Chaffee-Reece, Marlin, Remington-Keene, Boch, Trabue, Dean, and several others. The forty rifles were quickly whittled down to six by the normal system of tests. The three survivors of the supplementary tests, the Army having done everything it could think of to them, were the Lee, Chaffee-Reece, and the Hotchkiss. The testing board came to the conclusion that the three above-named rifles were suitable for service issue, and recommended them in the order named. General W. T. Sherman, spotting the Lee at the top of the list, suggested that the Secretary of War contract for fifty thousand dollars worth of the Lee, the amount of Congress' appropriation, and that one each of the Chaffee-Reece and the Hotchkiss be bought and placed in the Museum of Arms in Washington and a sort of certificate of merit be forwarded to their manufacturers. Sherman's recommendation was bucked right back to General Benét, who concluded that the three rifles were on par with one another, and that the fifty thousand dollars be split three ways to place the three rifles in the hands of troops for field tests. A tactful move, if nothing else.

The Lee rifle was different from its two competitors and all the others submitted to the board in that it had a detachable box magazine. Other than

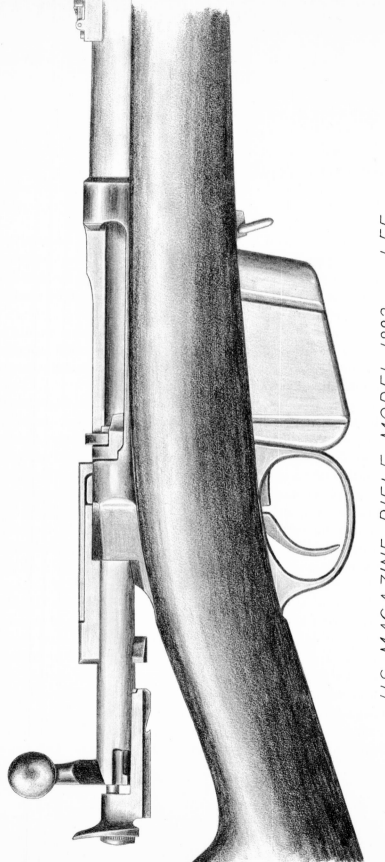

U.S. MAGAZINE RIFLE, MODEL 1882 —— LEE

SHIELDS

this unusual feature, its dimensions and operation were much the same as the various magazine arms tested for field use.

The Lee rifle receiver had a slot cut through it for receiving cartridges from the magazine, which was in a vertical well in front of the trigger guard and behind the receiver ring. The receiver contained a rotating bolt, and was cut away at the right side to form a shoulder for the bolt handle which, in conjunction with a lug on the left side of the receiver, locked the bolt in place. The bolt itself was composed of two main pieces, a bolt body, and a cocking piece, or hammer. The bolt body was hollowed out to house the firing pin, which was enclosed in a coil mainspring.

When the handle was turned up to unlock the bolt, the cocking piece was cammed to the rear, carrying with it the firing pin and withdrawing its tip within the bolt face. A cam surface at the front of the receiver forced the bolt slightly to the rear as it was turned, starting the empty case out of the chamber. Another cam, at the rear of the side cut of the receiver, forced the bolt forward as it was turned into its locked position.

The magazine was a sheet iron box containing a spring and follower which fed the cartridges up through the hole in the bottom of the receiver into the space traversed by the forward thrust of the bolt. The cartridges, held in the magazine in a single vertical column, were fed into the chamber as the bolt was unlocked and locked between shots. The magazine had to be removed if the rifle were to be used as a single-loader.

Like every United States rifle of its day, the Lee rifle chambered the .45-70 cartridge which, in the year prior to the rifle's adoption, was manufactured for the first time with a removable primer, allowing the empty shell case to be reloaded by the arsenal.

U.S. Magazine Rifle, Model 1882 (Chaffee-Reece)

SECOND on the list of the top rifles in the 1882 tests was the Chaffee-Reece rifle, the joint invention of R. S. Chaffee and General J. N. Reece.

It was a caliber .45 center-fire bolt action tubular magazine rifle, 49 inches long. The barrel was round, rifled with three grooves, and was 27.88 inches long. Near its muzzle was a lug which acted in the dual capacity of front sight base and bayonet stud. A sliding leaf rear sight, common to the three test rifles, was affixed to the barrel a short distance in front of the frame. Two oval steel bands held the stock to the barrel. As was common practice, the upper band held both the upper sling swivel and a stacking swivel. The lower sling swivel was on the front of the trigger guard. The receiver was stamped with U. S. Springfield 1884.

The breech mechanism of the Chaffee-Reece was of the turning-bolt type, made in two main components, a bolt body and a cocking piece. A firing pin, secured to the cocking piece and enclosed in a coil mainspring, was inserted into the hollow bolt body. The receiver was cut away to form the bolt shoulder, the point where the bolt handle rested when in its locked position. The bolt was unlocked by turning the bolt handle up to the left, the movement serving to cam back the cocking piece and withdraw the firing pin within the bolt face. A cam surface at the front of the receiver caused the bolt to move slightly to the rear as it was opened, providing the slow initial extraction so necessary with heavily loaded cartridges. As the bolt was returned to its locked position, another cam surface, formed by the shape of the side cut of the receiver, forced the bolt forward as it was locked, seating the cartridge under considerable pressure. Pressing the trigger withdrew the upper end of the trigger from the cocking piece and allowed the firing pin to drive forward and strike the cartridge primer.

The tubular magazine was fairly complex in design. A hole was bored in the rear end of the receiver, below the bolt and oblique to the axis of the bore. Through this hole the cartridges are fed from the magazine into the receiver, where the bolt rams them home into the chamber. As in the Hotchkiss design, the trigger was bent to fit around the magazine tube, which extended on a slope from the butt plate into the receiver.

The magazine proper consists of a metal tube and three bars or racks, the outer two of which are provided with rachet teeth. The bar on the right has a sliding motion, its object being to carry the cartridges forward a distance equal to the length of a single cartridge. The bar at the left has no longitudinal motion, and only serves to prevent cartridges from sliding to the rear after they have been carried forward. The center bar is capable only of short longitudinal movement, and is moved only when the loading gate in the butt plate is opened. It moves the other two bars down into an inoperative position and allows the magazine to be loaded with six cartridges. As

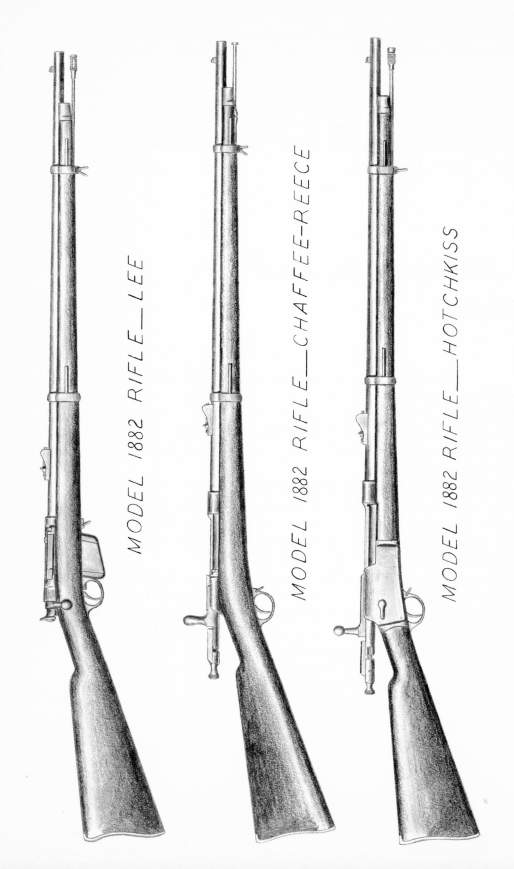

MODEL 1882 RIFLE — LEE

MODEL 1882 RIFLE — CHAFFEE-REECE

MODEL 1882 RIFLE — HOTCHKISS

SHIELDS

the bolt is opened, one bar moved high enough to allow one cartridge, held by its rachet tooth, to slip into the tooth of the opposite rack. Closing the bolt then moved the opposite bar. Each time the bolt was worked to extract and then load a cartridge, the cartridges in the magazine were moved forward the length of one cartridge, and so on, up the length of the tube and into the chamber. A magazine cutoff, which disengaged the magazine from working in conjunction with the bolt, allowed the rifle to be used as a single loader.

U.S. Magazine Rifle, Model 1882 (Hotchkiss)

THE third rifle on the acceptance list was the Hotchkiss rifle, submitted to the Army by the Winchester firm. It was an improved version of the rifle which had come out first in the tests for the Model 1878 rifle. In most outward respects it resembled the other two test rifles, in such particulars as sighting equipment, barrel bands, trigger guard dimensions, approximate weight, and length.

In other respects it was quite different from the others. The stock was made in two parts, a forestock and a buttstock. The tubular magazine was in the latter. The exterior of the receiver was of the form usually associated with lever action and other joined-stock arms, a flat-sided slab of steel which completely separated the two stock components.

The breech bolt was made in three pieces, a bolt head, bolt body, and a cocking piece. The bolt body was hollowed out to enclose the coil mainspring and a firing pin, which was threaded into the cocking piece. When the bolt was lifted, the cocking piece was cammed back beyond the nose of the sear, withdrawing the firing pin within the bolt head. When the bolt was locked, by turning the handle down into a cut in the receiver, the firing pin spring was compressed. By pressing the trigger, the sear was drawn away from the cocking piece and the firing pin, driven forward by the compressed spring, fired the cartridge.

The tubular magazine, located in the buttstock, was filled by pressing the cartridges into it from the receiver. The first cartridge bears against a detent. By pressing the trigger, the detent is depressed below the level of the magazine and the first cartridge, under pressure of the magazine spring, slips by and bears against the underside of the bolt. When the bolt is drawn back, this cartridge, under the impulse of the magazine spring, is fed into the chamber, while another cartridge moves against the detent. When the trigger is pulled to fire the first cartridge, the second one passes the detent and is in turn checked by the underside of the bolt. When the bolt is withdrawn to extract and eject the empty case, the second cartridge is forced into the feedway, to be picked up and locked in the chamber by the bolt, the operation being repeated until the magazine is empty. The usual required magazine cutoff was provided, to allow the piece to be used as a single-loader. The magazine capacity was five cartridges, and a single round could be carried in the chamber while the magazine was fully charged.

Winchester, who had held high hopes for this rifle, manufactured several hundred Hotchkiss rifles at their plant for the Army field trials. The Chaffee-Reece, having no company to build it, was manufactured at Springfield Armory and as such is the rifle usually referred to as the U. S. Rifle, Model 1882, for it bore the Armory stamps. Actually, the three rifles, the Lee, Chaffee-Reece, and Hotchkiss, received equal billing as far as the Army was concerned, and the place of manufacture of the Chaffee-Reece did not make it *the* Model 1882. The Lee rifle, due to the insolvency of its backers, was not made until 1884, when the Remington Company contracted to build it.

It was not until 1884, that the three rifles were ready for issue and field tests in the hands of regular troops. Trials went on during most of the year 1885. In 1886, the results were in and as tabulated among the one hundred and forty-nine companies to which the rifles were issued, the old, single-shot Springfield, the rifle already in service, was a clear-cut winner. Of the three magazine rifles, none of which approached the Springfield in popularity, the Lee rifle was the favorite among the troops.

In 1883, Winchester, in an attempt to capitalize on their rifle's apparent acceptance by the Army, manufactured the improved Hotchkiss as a commercial sporting rifle. Among civilians, it was received with something devoid of enthusiasm. Many years were to pass before the bolt action became popular.

The Smokeless Powder Era

THE evolution of firearms never proceeds at an even rate, for progress moves in spurts, as metallurgical and chemical advancements catch up with inventors' ideas. At such times the entire course of development is altered by various inventions which necessitate changes in all the weapons then considered the hottest things off the drafting tables. All of these changes had bitter enemies. The armored knight actually treated early firearms as something indecent, and gave way with the greatest reluctance to the uncouth and unarmored peasant who could shoot him out of the saddle with a crude musket and thus make knighthood a less advantageous calling. The muzzle-loading enthusiast hooted with derision as the breech-loader crowded his weapon out of existence. But such things as the discovery of gunpowder, the invention of the mercuric percussion cap, the conception of the metallic cartridge, all forced drastic revisions, sooner or later, in weapons manufacture and design. And in 1884, Paul Vieille, a French chemist, invented smokeless powder.

Black powder, for over six hundred years after its discovery, was the only successful propellant known. The nature of its composition, two easily ignited fuels and an oxidizing agent, greatly limited the effectiveness of firearms used with it. A black powder explosion does not convert all of the solid matter into gas, but produces a dense cloud of smoke and deposits a large quantity of solid residue in the gun barrel, fouling the rifling badly. Its use also imposed severe limitations on velocity and range. Due to its burning characteristics, black powder is not well-adapted to producing high velocity, to put it mildly. A low velocity bullet has but little kinetic energy, and must rely on its mass to do the damage. This limitation is a serious one, from several considerations. For one thing, kinetic energy varies with the square of the velocity. If you triple the velocity, you increase the energy nine times; and all other factors being equal, the faster bullet will be nine times as hard to stop. Furthermore, the more slowly a bullet travels, the more it drops per unit distance, since gravity pulls it earthward at a given rate of acceleration.

The faster it drops, the higher the muzzle must be raised in order to make the bullet connect with the target as the range increases. The only way to overcome this is to decrease the time between the bullet's departure and its arrival at the target; in short, to increase its starting or muzzle velocity. And black powder did not lend itself well to high velocities. One disadvantage reinforced another, and the black powder rifles of the 1880's represented the probable limit of development until a new propellant was found.

Smokeless powder did not come along all at once, like the hidden answer to a rebus; its antecedents go back a number of years. Nitroglycerine, an ingredient of many modern powders, is an old explosive, made famous in 1846 by Alfred Nobel. It is a highly unstable compound, always seeking to rearrange itself into more stable ones, namely, large quantities of gas. It is useless as a propellant. It is sensitive beyond belief and explodes at all sorts of embarrassing moments, almost instantaneously and with incredible violence. A similarly violent explosive is guncotton or nitrocellulose, formed by the action of sulphuric and nitric acids upon cotton, itself almost pure cellulose. Guncotton, when used alone, is also too unstable and fast-burning to be used as a propellant.

Eventually, it was discovered that the burning rate of guncotton could be lowered by gelatinizing it in acetone or mixtures of alcohol and ether. The resulting plastic mass, stabilized against deterioration by the addition of a compound such as diphenylamine, an analine derivative, could be moulded into grains of suitable size and used as a propellant. When this compound is ignited, the combustion products are practically all gases, eliminating both smoke and powder fouling. Another common type is made by absorbing nitroglycerine in guncotton. This powder, known as double-base powder, burns faster than the single base nitrocellulose propellants, and its use in modern U. S. firearms is confined to caliber .45 pistols, shotgun loads, and carbine ammunition. One of the early successful double base powders, made famous by the British, consisted of nitroglycerine absorbed in guncotton and a small percentage of petroleum jelly. It was mixed with acetone to form a paste, and was extruded through a die in long strings, like spaghetti. In this form it is called Cordite. These propellants, all familiar to the firearms trade today, were closely guarded secrets in the 1880's.

Extreme care must be exercised in the manufacture of smokeless powder, not merely because of the obvious explosives hazards, but because the quantity of gas produced by smokeless powder is dependent upon the surface area free to burn. As only the exposed surface burns, each grain must be made accurately, in exact shapes and sizes, to avoid exceeding the maximum permissible chamber pressure for whatever weapon its use is intended. But this powder, though neither entirely smokeless nor powder, for that matter, is vastly superior to the old black powder. It is safe to store in large quantities and will burn, not explode, if ignited in the open. It produces little powder smoke and almost no powder ashes. But its outstanding quality is the fact that it is a slow explosive, its initial burning speed being controlled by the amount of solvent, and can be made to burn at some predetermined rate. Its rate of combustion can be attenuated, so that the bullet could be started slowly into the rifling and then accelerated until it reached a maximum velocity near the muzzle. A bullet is made to move by the pressure caused by gas expanding behind it. This pressure must not be allowed to drop too rapidly, for at the instant of firing, the total volume available for gas expansion is the interior of the cartridge case. As the bullet moves forward, the gas is free to occupy that part of the barrel already traversed by the bullet. Pressure will then drop, unless the evolution of gas is accelerated enough to maintain pressure, although the volume into which it expands is progressively increasing.

Although the ease with which a propellant burns is determined by the amount of solvent in it, the rate of burning, at constant pressure, is proportional to the surface area free to burn. In practice, powders are made to burn either degressively, neutrally, or progressively. Degressive powder, such as a strip or solid cylinder of explosive, will undergo a reduction of surface area as it burns, and its relative evolution of gas decreases as it consumes itself. Neutral powders, which form the majority of U. S. shoulder arm propellants, are made as single perforated cylinders. As a monoperforated grain burns, its outer surface decreases, while its inner surface increases at the same rate. The total surface area remains about the same, giving rise to the name neutral. Progressive powders, ordinarily used in artillery, are made in the form of multiperforated grains whose total surface area increases as the grains burn.

The tremendous pressure rise produced by neutral rifle powder is caused by its sensitivity to confinement. Unconfined powder, such as powder ignited in the open, will burn rather slowly, with intense heat, but no explosion. But within a gun barrel, where the gases cannot escape or dissipate their heat, the burning becomes extremely rapid. When ignited by the primer, the grains begin to burn, producing heated gases. This causes a rise in pressure, which increases the heat, which increases the rate of combustion, which in turn produces still higher pressure and more heat, until something has to give. This rapid and almost astronomic buildup of pressure is relieved by driving the bullet forward. The tighter smokeless powder is confined, the faster it burns, and in a rough way, the relative confinement is determined by the caliber and weight of the bullet in front of the powder charge. It is this ability to utilize available gas which enables smokeless powder to produce high velocities while holding pressures within safe limits. The bullet is forced into the rifling while pressure is still fairly low, and then begins its colossal acceleration as rising pressure drives it down the barrel. Pressure continues to rise in spite of the increase in volume, as the rate of pressure increase spirals upward. After only a few inches of movement, maximum pressure is reached; a fraction of a second later all the powder is consumed, and the bullet continues to move as the pressurized incandescent gas continues to expand. The continued expansion without renewal of heat serves to lower the pressure and cool the gases, so that by the time the bullet reaches the muzzle, pressure has dropped to about a fifth of the maximum level, and the gas has cooled from about three thousand degrees to a point where it produces no flash by daylight. Quite a different story from black powder, which imparted a hammerlike blow to the bullet, and often consumed itself after the bullet had cleared the muzzle. Black powder could, if need be, produce fairly high velocities, by the simple expedient of using more black powder, but the resulting pressures were dangerously high.

One change always brings on another, and the new propellant required many modifications in bullet design. Smokeless powder was potentially capable of firing bullets at high speeds. But high velocity, coupled with large heavy bullets means intolerable recoil, and a good chance of destroying the rifle. The obvious solution is to reduce bullet weight. But simply cutting off the base of a large caliber bullet to reduce weight is *not* the answer. A stubby bullet might be light enough, but it would expose a large cross sectional area to air resistance, without enough weight in relation to its diameter. This relationship, known as sectional density, is represented by dividing the bullet's weight by the square of its diameter (W/D^2) and is the chief factor in a bullet's attempt to maintain its original velocity, despite air retardation. Thus the high velocity bullet was made small in caliber and very long in proportion to its diameter. Its nose was later sharply pointed, in an effort to further reduce air resistance.

However, all was not peaches and cream—not yet. The high velocity bullet, being of small diameter, can be stabilized in flight only by increasing its rate of rotation in proportion to the decrease in diameter. The caliber .45 rifle of the 1870's was rifled with a twist of about one turn in every 2 feet;

a modern caliber .30 rifle requires a twist of one turn in 10 inches, which gives it a rotational speed of several thousand revolutions per second. Yet this represents a fairly delicate design compromise. If a spherical projectile is fired into the air, it may tumble without affecting its trajectory too much, because the same surface is always presented to the air. But long pointed projectiles must always point towards the target if velocity and range are to be considered. A bullet maintains its balance by means of its high rotational speed, much as a spinning top, ordinarily completely unstable, remains balanced on its point. The gyroscopic stability imparted to it by its spin serves to keep it pointed correctly, and it would seem that the greater the rotational speed, the better the stability.

It can be carried too far; if the projectile spins too rapidly, it will tend to point in exactly the same direction as the gun barrel, while its path of flight must eventually descend towards the earth. As its own trajectory drops out from under it, the overstabilized projectile is left pointing skyward while it is dropping earthward; its effective direction is sideways, with a complete loss of accuracy and range. The bullet performs another odd motion while in flight. Getting back to our spinning top analogy, we notice that the top never remains vertical, but wobbles about its axis as it spins. A bullet does the same; its point is first on one side of its trajectory, then on another. This wobble, called precession, is extremely noticeable when firing tracers, which makes visible the looping motion and makes one wonder about the old bromide "straight as a bullet."

Though the highest attainable rotational speeds are far from desirable in a spin-stabilized projectile, the necessary speed is high enough to rule out lead as the bullet composition. In spite of the slow initial start of the smokeless powder explosion, a lead bullet, even a hardened one, would tend to strip through the rifling instead of turning with it, because of the rapid twist, heat, and friction. The lead bullet, therefore, had to be jacketed with a harder metal. Steel, the obvious choice, proved to be too hard on rifle barrels, and was succeeded by experimental jackets of pure copper and German Silver. The Service finally settled on cupronickel, an alloy of copper and nickel. Cupronickel, our standard bullet jacket for some years, unfortunately deposited small lumps of metal in the bore, which were difficult to remove. We had rid ourselves of the curse of powder fouling and inherited metal fouling. There's always something. It was not until 1925, and the adoption of gilding metal (an alloy of copper and zinc) as a bullet jacket, that smokeless powder ammunition approached the high state of development it reaches today. Gilding metal also leaves a deposit in the bore, but in the form of a thin copper wash, which seems to have no detrimental effect on accuracy.

As a result of Vieille's discovery, France, in 1886, adopted the Lebel magazine rifle, remarkable for its small caliber, 8 mm, and the smokeless powder it employed. The race was on, and the United States was left at the starting gate with its old charcoal burner, the single shot trapdoor action Springfield. Japan, of all nations, was the second country to follow the new trend in rifles. Close behind came Great Britain, Germany, and Austria, in 1888. By 1891, virtually all the major powers were armed with some version of the high velocity rifle, with the sole exception of the United States. The usual reason given is that the United States, for some years, was unable to unravel the secret of smokeless powder. That may be. However, at the end of the Spanish-American War there was an interesting but now forgotten squabble over just why the United States was so short of smokeless powder during that war when other nations seemed to be doing so well with it. It was quite a show. The Army blamed Congress and Congress blamed the Army. All it needed was telecasting to make real headline material out of it. The reasons advanced for the shortage, and contradictory reasons they were, resulting from hearings conducted before the Senate Subcommittee of Appropriations in April, 1900. One, Captain I. N. Lewis, when questioned by Senator Teller, replied as follows: "In my opinion, it was the direct result of our present policy, in regard to all military inventions and their development. We have tried to form a closed corporation within ourselves. The opportunities and facilities for original experimental work are limited to a very few, and those few are not in sympathetic touch, as they should be, with outside developments." On winter evenings, I used to wonder what became of the Captain's career. However, he seems to have survived his own remarks and went on to invent the Lewis machine gun, made a pot full of money at it, and maintained a fine running battle with the Army brass throughout his career.

Another way of looking at it was expressed by O. B. Mitcham, an Army Ordnance captain. In a letter covering the same subject matter he stated that "Smokeless powders, unlike black powders, cannot be produced in one day, two days, or a week. Even after a satisfactory size and form of grain have been determined for a gun, a length of time varying from three to four weeks for powders for small calibers and up to three months for powders for larger calibers is required to thoroughly remove the solvent by drying. Up to a recent date there was no supply of smokeless powders for either the

[144]

Army or the Navy. This was not the fault of the Army or Navy officers, but due to the well-known failure of Congress to provide money. Now that funds are available, it is seen that no serious difficulty has been experienced in obtaining satisfactory results." Take your pick.

U. S. Magazine Rifle, Model 1892 (Krag-Jörgensen)

IN 1888, the Army, after having experimented briefly with compressed and perforated black powder in an attempt to produce a high velocity cartridge, gave the whole business up as a bad job; the chamber pressure was always too high for the velocity it gave. In that same year, the Chief of Ordnance noted that the results obtained in France with the Lebel rifle seemed to point to a radical innovation in powder manufacture. It sure did. A couple of years went by before American commercial chemical concerns solved the mystery. In November, 1890, a testing board was convened, and fifty-three rifles were entered into competition to decide which one would become the United States service rifle. Many foreign rifles, the service arms for countries which already had smokeless powder magazine rifles, were entered into the tests: the Belgian Mauser, Model 1888 German rifle, Japanese Murata, the Austrian and Roumanian Mannlichers, British Lee, Danish Krag-Jörgensen, plus a number of others. Among the American rifles were the Savage lever action, Chaffee-Reece, and some hopeless designs such as the Sporer, whose cartridges were held in a vertically staggered group in the buttstock and were fed into the chamber via a long tube from the magazine into the receiver.

Testing was done in the now-familiar way, but with a view towards putting the magazine feed systems through their paces. Unfortunately, great emphasis was placed on each magazine rifle's ability to fire as a single loader.

The model adopted was the Krag-Jörgensen, a slight modification of the system used by Denmark. The magazine of this rifle was unique, being constructed horizontally, and loose rounds were loaded through the right side of

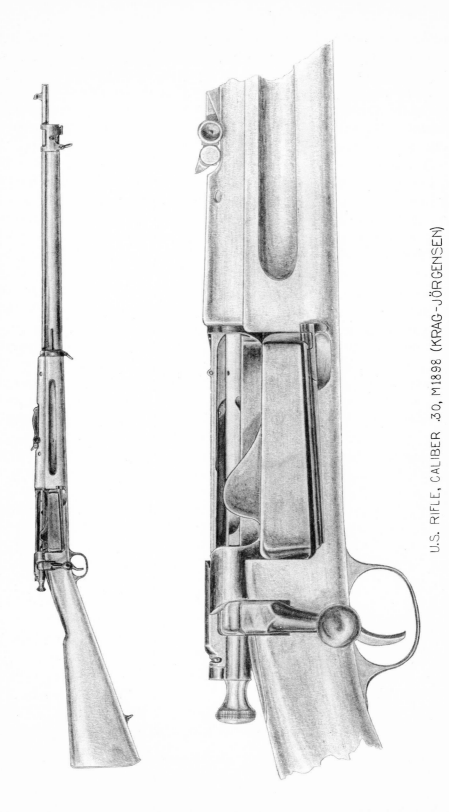

U.S. RIFLE, CALIBER .30, M1898 (KRAG-JÖRGENSEN)

the rifle. The right face of the magazine could be swung outward and down, to act as a loading gate. When the gate was closed, a follower spring forced the cartridges to the left and up, to be seated in the chamber as the bolt was pushed forward. A magazine cutoff, mounted on the left side of the receiver, allowed the rifle to be used as a single-loader, with the loaded magazine held in reserve. The Krag had an exceptionally smooth action, and except for the awkward projecting magazine, was easy to handle.

The action was strong and reliable. Locking was performed by a locking lug at the front end of the bolt, locking the breech directly behind the cartridge. The face of the bolt was recessed and completely enclosed the base of the cartridge case. This feature came out recently in commercial Remington bolt action rifles, heralded as a marvelous safety, which it is. Actually, the basic principle is well over a half century old. The bolt handle projects past the right side of the stock, turned down out of the way. The locking recess and the rear of the receiver bridge are built as cam surfaces. As the bolt handle is pulled upward to unlock the action, the bolt rotates through a large arc and moves rearward a short distance, providing the leverage necessary to free the fired cartridge case from the walls of the chamber. This feature of slow initial extraction is mandatory for all high power rifles, since the brass case swells when the rifle is fired. It sticks to the chamber walls and must be, in effect, pried loose without breaking off the rear of the cartridge case. The extractor lies along the top of the bolt body, terminating in a claw which rides over the rim of the cartridge.

The cartridge, our first smokeless powder round, is variously known as the .30-40 Krag and Caliber .30 United States Army. The drawn brass case was of rimmed bottlenecked design, loaded with a charge of single base nitroglycerine powder which varied between thirty-five and forty-two grains. The bullet, a core of lead and tin composition jacketed with cupronickel, was circled with three annular lubricating grooves; the mouth of the case was crimped into the front groove to secure the bullet. The completed bullet, weighing two hundred and twenty grains, was flat-based and round-nosed in form. The primer consisted of three main parts, a cup, a brass anvil, and a waterproofed paper disc. The cup, made of cartridge copper, contained the priming compound, covered and waterproofed by the disc. The anvil was circular with two small semicircular portions, which served as vents, removed from each side. The primer filler was composed of sulphur, antimony sulphide, potassium chlorate, and powdered glass. The combination of a two hundred and twenty grain bullet and 2000 feet/second muzzle velocity added up to a very potent round.

[147]

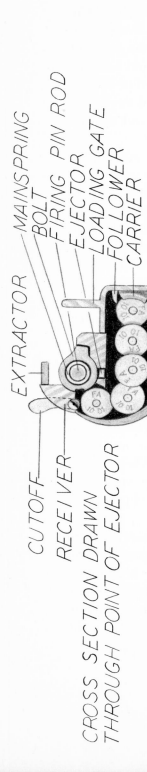

EXTRACTOR
MAINSPRING
BOLT
FIRING PIN ROD
EJECTOR
LOADING GATE
FOLLOWER
CARRIER

CUTOFF
RECEIVER

CROSS SECTION DRAWN
THROUGH POINT OF EJECTOR

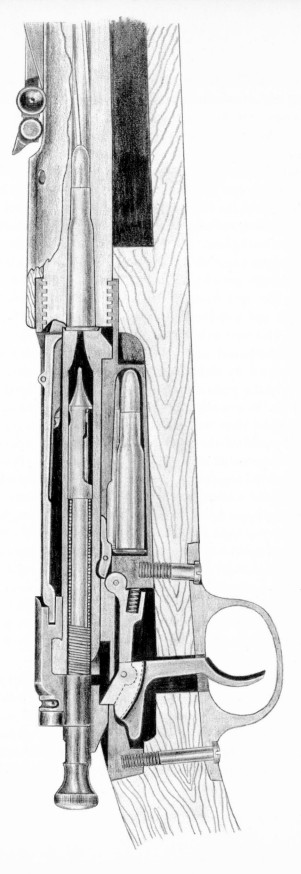

SECTIONAL VIEW OF M1898 KRAG-JÖRGENSEN

SHIELDS

Although the Krag rifle was modified several times between its adoption and discontinuance, the following characteristics are common to all the various models.

The caliber was .30-inch, center-fire. The 30-inch-round barrel was rifled with four grooves, making one turn to the right every ten inches. The total length of the rifle was 49 inches; weight about nine pounds, five ounces. The stock was 46 inches long, held to the barrel by two bands, the upper of which held the bayonet stud and stacking swivel. The lower band held the upper sling swivel. The lower swivel was mounted just forward of the toe of the butt plate. All metal parts were dark-blued. The rifle, of five-round magazine capacity, was equipped with adjustable rear sights and a blade front sight on a high base which was welded to the barrel.

The first model Krag-Jörgensen, the Model 1892, had a solid upper band, and a sliding leaf rear sight, adjustable from 100 to 1900 yards.

The next model, the Model 1896, had an upper band with two straps over the barrel, and a different rear sight which could be elevated with the leaf down, by sliding it up a pair of inclined ramps. The model date, in addition to the manufacturing armory, was stamped on the left side of the receiver. Practically all of the Model 1892s were altered at Springfield Armory to Model 1896, and the original 1892 model is a pretty rare bird. The magazine cutoff of the Model 1896 was built to open the magazine for feeding when the cutoff thumbpiece was down. The thumbpiece, located on the left side of the receiver, had a spindle which occupied a groove in the wall of the magazine well when the thumbpiece was down; in this position it allowed the top cartridge to rise high enough to be caught by the bolt in its forward movement and be pushed into the chamber. When the thumbpiece was turned up, the spindle protruded into the magazine well, preventing the top cartridge from riding high enough to be caught by the bolt. The safety of all Krag rifles was located at the top rear portion of the bolt sleeve, and could be turned through a one hundred and eighty degree arc. When turned horizontally to the left it allowed the rifle to fire; when either vertical or horizontal to the right it engaged a notch in the firing pin rod and prevented any movement of the rod or striker.

The Model 1898, the final rifle model, had a bolt handle seat set flush with the receiver. The new rear sight had a solid center leaf, graduated up to 2000 yards in increments of 100 yards and was also capable of windage adjustment. The magazine cutoff was altered to allow the magazine to function when the thumbpiece was up, and held inoperative when the thumbpiece was down ... the exact reverse of that of the previous Model 1896. The

Krag action was certainly handy, as far as loading was concerned; the magazine could be charged with the bolt closed or open, with the cutoff up or down, or if one or more cartridges had been fired, the partially empty magazine could be refilled without emptying the loaded chamber.

In October, 1894, the Fourth Infantry received its full quota of Model 1892 Krag-Jörgensen rifles, and was the first unit in the United States Army to be so equipped. Their issue amounted to field tests, for the structural changes that were recommended were soon incorporated in the Model 1896. All told, over three hundred and sixteen thousand Krags were made between 1894 and 1904, when their manufacture was discontinued in favor of the Mauser-type bolt action system.

Winchester Magazine Rifle, Model 1895

IN THE 1880's, John Browning, the American gun-designing wizard who had designed the popular Winchester Model 1886 rifle, came up with a lever action rifle capable of handling the enormously powerful smokeless powder military cartridges which had just come into being. Browning had invented or was due to invent just about everything you could think of, including Colt automatic pistols, the BAR, Browning machine guns, and automatic shotguns, and his new rifle was an attempt to keep the lever action rifle apace of the strong dependable bolt action military rifles which had become the universal fighting tools of the world's armies. The design was built by the Winchester Company, who chambered it for the .30-40 Krag cartridge, the service cartridge then in use. Later it was chambered for the 6 mm Navy cartridge, and still later the .30-06 and virtually all the domestic big game cartridges of its day.

As adopted for military use, it was a caliber .30 center-fire rifle, with a 28-inch-round, steel barrel. In general appearance it was similar to the earlier lever action rifles, except that the tubular magazine had been replaced by the Lee vertical box magazine which protruded past the bottom of the frame. The stock was in two sections, a buttstock and a military length forestock which extended to within several inches of the muzzle. Two bands

WINCHESTER REPEATING RIFLE, MODEL 1895

held the forestock to the barrel, a wide two-strap upper band with a bayonet stud and a stacking swivel, and a lower oval band which carried the upper sling swivel; the lower swivel was attached to the front of the magazine. A wooden handguard covered the barrel from the frame to the lower band. A front sight blade, set in a high base, was brazed onto the barrel near the muzzle. The rear sight, a flat adjustable leaf, was mounted on the handguard.

Although the rifle took a heavy cartridge and was fed through a box magazine, it operated much like the earlier lever action rifles, in that the functions of loading, locking, extraction, ejection, and cocking were all done by one movement of a lever which also served as a trigger guard.

In 1898, the Secretary of War ordered ten thousand Winchester Model 1895 rifles for issue to the Army, overriding the protests of the Ordnance Department, which wanted no part of a lever action rifle. Ordnance had just turned down a lever action rifle, the Savage, during the 1890 trials. They already had a good service rifle and were cooking up a better one. About a hundred Model 1895's were shipped to the Philippines for trial and were soon returned as unserviceable for field use.

In its day the Model 1895 was extremely popular as a civilian big game rifle. The public had as yet not taken to the bolt action rifle, as Wincheseter found out after trying to market the Hotchkiss rifle. Anyway, the Army was the only outfit producing bolt action rifles. The Model '95 Winchester filled the vacancy quite nicely until after World War I, when the Mauser action came into wide commercial use. The Model '95 may be found today in military form in quite a lot of foreign calibers, for it was sold to any nation who wished to buy it as a military arm. In World War I, Russia bought over a quarter of a million of them, chambered for the 7.62 mm Russian cartridge.

Today, though no longer manufactured, the Model 1895, alone among the lever actions, can be classed with the bolt action weapons which are chambered for cartridges of military size.

U.S. Rifle, Caliber .30, Model 1903

THE Krag-Jörgensen, though possessing a smoothness of action still unsurpassed in bolt action rifles, was rendered obsolescent at the turn of the century by the superiority of the German Mauser rifle. In the late 1860's, two German brothers, Paul and Wilhelm Mauser, had pioneered a bolt action rifle which could cock itself by cam action as the breech was opened between shots. They began designing and building rifles in the black powder days, and their products invariably kept pace with, and were usually ahead of, those of other designers. As the nineteenth century drew to a close, they had developed a rifle so fundamentally correct in design that no major improvements have been made on it to this day. Most nations eventually adopted the Mauser rifle in one form or another. The self-cocking bolt, the long elastic extractor, the camming principle of slowly freeing the expanded cartridge case from its chamber, are all distinctive Mauser innovations.

The Mauser concern sold its products both in Germany and abroad, and Spain was one of its eager customers. During the Spanish-American War, the American Krag-Jörgensen rifle was pitted against the clip-fed Modelo Espanol Mauser, a 7 mm rifle supplied to Spain by the Mauser Company. The Spanish Mauser outclassed the Krag as a military weapon. At San Juan Hill, a force of about seven hundred Spaniards inflicted over fourteen hundred casualties on the American infantry before being overwhelmed by assault.

For one thing, the Krag was loaded with loose rounds, the theory being that the rifle was to be used as a single-shot weapon until such time as a great volume of fire was needed. Then the magazine cutoff was released and the full magazine (used as a sort of reserve supply) was utilized. This idea, never a very good one, haunted our ordnance design up to the adoption of the M1 rifle. The Spaniards, who could load their rifles five cartridges at a time, used their magazine rifle for what it was, a weapon capable of delivering a great volume of accurate fire. As important too, were the Mauser rifle's advantages of twin opposed locking lugs, positive extraction, and space-saving rimless ammunition.

U.S. RIFLE, CALIBER .30, M1903

M1903 REAR SIGHT

M1903A3 REAR SIGHT

The United States, to its credit, was quick to realize that a change was in order. In 1900, a board was organized to test our newly designed rifle, a frank copy of the German Mauser system. Manufacturing rights were later purchased from the Mauser Company for two hundred thousand dollars. This Model 1901 was a .30 caliber Mauser with a barrel 29.5 inches long, a 41.5-inch stock, and an over-all length of about 50 inches. An order for five thousand rifles was placed with Springfield Armory as soon as trials for this experimental weapon had been completed. However, the performance of the new rifles on hand had been so satisfactory that it was decided to adopt it for service without going through the process of a field trial of the five thousand rifles. Accordingly, a board was convened, which recommended several changes to be incorporated in the rifle before it went into full scale production. Among these changes were:

1) reduction of barrel length from 29.5 to 24 inches
2) rear sight moved to rear against the receiver and secured to the barrel by a sleeve, doing away with the screws formerly used
3) wooden handguard extended forward to the upper band
4) oiler and thong added, located in a trap in the butt plate
5) area of bearing surface of the rear bolt lug in receiver was increased
6) a spring catch was added to prevent the bolt from slipping forward under the clip seat when the arm was held with the barrel inclined downward.

The Chief of Ordnance recommended the adoption and manufacture of this rifle, and his recommendation was approved by the Secretary of War on June 19, 1903.

The cartridge, except for being rimless, closely resembled the original Krag ammunition, having a two hundred and twenty grain round-nosed bullet, and forty-three grains of smokeless powder. The muzzle velocity was about 2300 feet/second.

In 1906, the ammunition was vastly improved. The bullet was redesigned with a double-arc spitzer point, and its weight was reduced to one hundred and fifty grains. The propellent weight was increased to forty-nine grains, muzzle velocity was boosted to 2700 feet/second, and extreme range was, in theory, anyway, almost three miles. This was the famous cartridge commonly called the .30-06, the numbers "06" representing the last two digits of the year of its adoption, 1906. The pointed bullet was shorter than the old round-nosed one, and the rifles themselves had to be altered to chamber the new cartridges. This was done by removing the barrels, cutting off the rear two threads at the breech end, reinserting the barrels, and reaming out the chamber to new dimensions. Existing M1903 rifles were recalled to

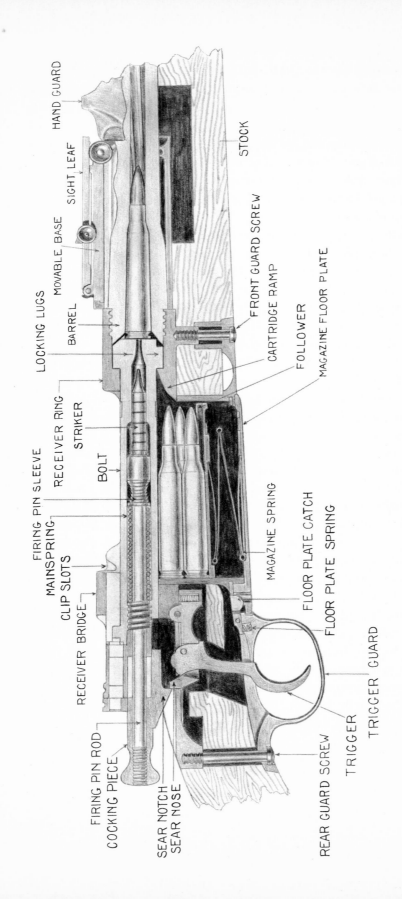

SECTIONAL VIEW OF U.S. RIFLE, CALIBER .30, M1903

the Armory, rebarreled for the .30-06 cartridge and fitted with a new rear sight graduated for 2850 yards, to compensate for the changed ballistic properties. The final product is probably the best bolt action military rifle ever made, short, dependable, foolproof, and enormously powerful.

As made from 1906 on, the M1903 rifle is 43.2 inches long, with a 41.5-inch black walnut stock. The barrel is 24 inches long, bored to .30 inch, and rifled with four grooves which twist uniformly to the right at a rate of one turn in 10 inches. Each groove is .004-inch deep, making the total bore diameter, measured across the grooves, .308 inch. Total weight is about eight and six-tenths pounds; all metal parts are dark blued. The M1903 was manufactured at Springfield Armory and Rock Island Arsenal, the receiver ring being marked with the letters U.S., the name of the manufacturer, followed by the words Model 1903, and the serial number.

All the objectionable features of the Krag were eliminated. To load the M1903, one flipped the magazine cutoff (oh yes, we still had one) to the on position and pulled the bolt to its rearmost position. A clip of five cartridges was inserted in a set of slots milled in the receiver bridge. The cartridges were stripped off the clip into the magazine, where they were automatically arranged in a three-and-two staggered formation. The clip was pulled out and thrown away, and the bolt was pushed forward and locked, readying the rifle for firing.

The magazine is a vertical well at the rear of the barrel. The bottom is closed by a removable floor plate, on top of which is seated a Z-spring and a follower. The insertion of cartridges into the magazine compresses the spring and furnishes power for feeding cartridges into the position where they are picked up by the bolt. The heart of the rifle is the Mauser bolt, which has two opposed locking lugs at its forward end. There is also a third, or safety lug, which bears against the forward face of the receiver bridge. The extractor is a heavy but flexible claw which extends almost the entire length of the bolt body. The bolt body is hollow, and contains a firing pin rod and striker, encircled by a coil spring. As the bolt handle is lifted after each shot, the bolt is cammed back a short distance, freeing the swollen cartridge case from the chamber. At the same time, the cocking piece, whose sear notch rides in a groove in the receiver tang, is prevented from turning. It is forced rearward, compressing the coil mainspring and withdrawing the firing pin from the face of the bolt. The ninety degree turn of the bolt forces the sear notch to engage a notch at the rear of the bolt and holds the mainspring compressed.

As the bolt is pulled rearward, the extractor pulls the empty case clear of the chamber; and the ejector, a thin metal plate on the left of the inside of the receiver, rides through a groove cut in the left hand locking lug. The cartridge case, held on the right side by the extractor and struck on the left by the ejector, pivots around the extractor claw and is flipped clear of the rifle.

When the bolt is pushed forward, the bottom of the bolt face engages the top cartridge in the magazine, and pushes it into the chamber as the extractor claw snaps into the extracting cannelure of the cartridge. Turning the bolt handle down to the right engages the locking lugs in their recesses. The sear notch, meanwhile, is released from the notch in the bolt, but is engaged by the sear. Pressing the trigger depresses the sear and allows the firing pin to drive forward, firing the cartridge.

World War I brought to us the realization that our '06 ammunition left something to be desired; the ballistics tables looked fine, but the cartridge never did what was expected of it. In 1925, it was improved into a formidably healthy round, a one hundred and seventy-two grain boat-tail bullet, jacketed with gilding metal. This new cartridge, known as the M1, was accepted as standard. It was not issued out until 1936, after the stock of old ammunition was used up, but its appearance produced a totally unexpected trouble—it shot too far. United States Army and National Guard rifle ranges do not employ any vertical backstop, but are constructed so that fired bullets are allowed to continue traveling until they run out of energy. The impact areas of these ranges turned out to be too small to contain the boat-tail ammunition. Consequently, there was a reversion back to the old .30-06 fodder, equipped with a gilding metal jacket. There were some minor changes made in the round; the maximum bullet weight was increased to one hundred and fifty-two grains, and the muzzle velocity was boosted to 2800 feet/second. This cartridge, known as the M2, is our present service round.

The M1903 rifle was manufactured virtually without change until 1928, when a few improvements were made on the rifle. This new product, known as the M1903A1, is a standard '03, with the sole exception of the stock, which has a pistol grip intended to improve the midget buttstock of the M1903. The finger grooves in the stock were eliminated, and the butt plate was checkered to provide a better grip on the shoulder.

The second modification, the M1903A2, was not a shoulder arm at all, but a stripped down rifle used as a subcaliber device for tank and artillery gunnery. It is hardly a familiar weapon, even to Army personnel.

When World War II rolled around, the M1 rifle was our standard shoulder arm, but due to our meager stock of M1's and limited production fa-

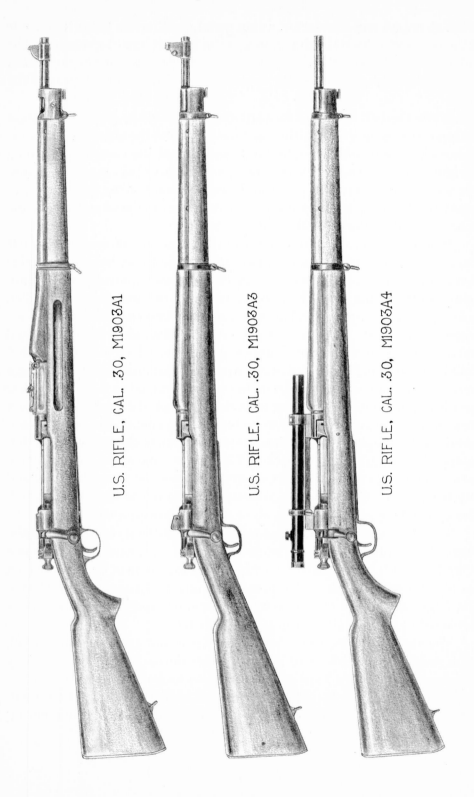

U.S. RIFLE, CAL. .30, M1903A1

U.S. RIFLE, CAL. .30, M1903A3

U.S. RIFLE, CAL. .30, M1903A4

SHIELDS

cilities, contracts were let out to commercial concerns to produce a wartime version of the M1903. The chief difference between the two rifles is a change in location of the rear sights. The rear sight of the M1903A3 is of a wing type mounted on the receiver bridge. It is adjustable by means of clicks, each click, whether for windage or elevation, representing a change in minutes of angle. The elevation scale is graduated in one-minute increments, and the windage scale moves in four-minute graduations. The other changes are those designed to facilitate rapid production. Most of the barrels are rifled with two grooves instead of the customary four, which does not materially affect accuracy. Many of the metal parts, such as bands, trigger guards, swivels, and magazine floor plates; are made of sheet metal stampings, instead of being machined. The use of pistolgrip or straight stocks appears to have been optional with the manufacturer.

The last modification of the M1903 was the M1903A4, a World War II snipers' rifle. It was an M1903A3 with the front and rear sights removed, and a commercial telescopic sight, usually a 2.20 power Weaver scope, was affixed to a bridge mount over the receiver. The bolt handle was bent so it could clear the scope each time it was lifted. The presence of the telescopic sight prevented the use of clip-loading.

A word about safety; the early M1903 receivers were intended for use with early ammunition, and were often the products of imperfect heat-treatment. These old receivers were sometimes about as hard as glass and often just as brittle. Those M1903's made at Springfield Armory with a serial number under eight hundred thousand, and those made at Rock Island Arsenal with a number under two hundred and eighty-five thousand, five hundred and seven, are doubtful risks when used with modern ammunition. All later receivers were either double heat-treated or made of nickel steel, and are perfectly safe. Correct head space in these early rifles is *not* a guarantee of safety; the fault lies in the heat treatment of the receiver itself.

U.S. Magazine Rifle, Model 1917 (Enfield)

GREAT BRITAIN, at the start of World War I, found itself confronted with the same problem which had often beset the United States; the nation was incapable of arming its forces in the short time span made necessary by the war emergency. The British turned to several American commercial firms to produce their pattern 1914 rifle, commonly known as the Enfield. Three enormous plants contracted to do the work; the Eddystone plant, owned by the Remington Arms Company of Delaware, Winchester Repeating Arms Company, and the Remington Arms Company of Ilion, New York. However, the plants were disappointingly slow in turning out production and by the time they were in full operation, Britain had solved most of her own troubles and early in 1917, began to slack off on her demands.

In March, 1917, the United States entered the war, as usual, with a microscopic Army and no facilities for quick expansion. The Model 1903 Springfield, our standard issue rifle, was being produced by Springfield Armory and Rock Island Arsenal, but in insufficient quantity to equip the wartime army.

It was only through sheer luck that three commercial firms were tooled up to produce a military rifle, but there they were, and the supply difficulty was overcome by altering the Enfield slightly and chambering it for the United States caliber .30 cartridge. Luckily, the two rifles were quite similar; each was a Mauser action, caliber .30, with a vertical staggered clip-fed magazine and roughly the same outward dimensions as the other. The Enfield was altered to the American cartridge by boring the barrel to American caliber .30, chambering the barrel for the U.S. round, changing the bolt face to take a rimless cartridge, and lengthening the magazine to accept the slightly longer American round.

The American product, known as the U. S. Rifle, caliber .30, Model 1917, was a bolt action magazine rifle with a 26-inch-round steel barrel, rifled with five grooves which made one left hand turn in ten inches. The 42.88-inch

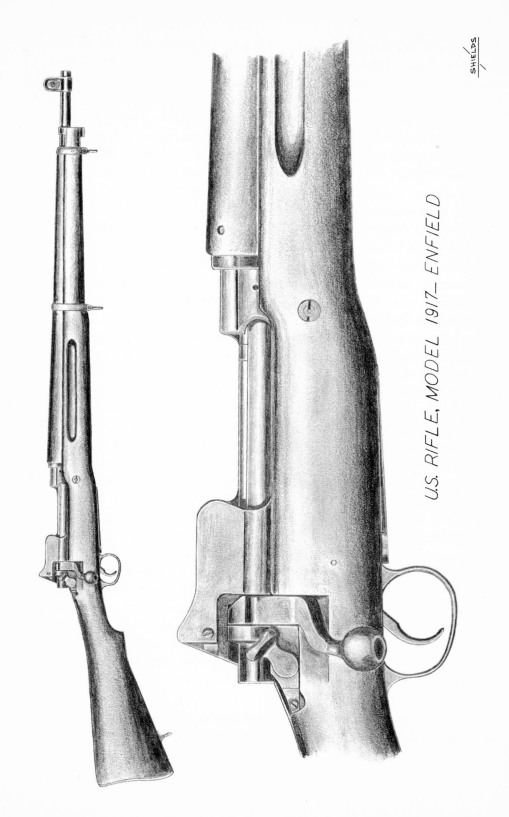

U.S. RIFLE, MODEL 1917 _ ENFIELD

SHIELDS

stock was of full military length, with a small pistol grip and two finger grooves in front of the receiver and behind the lower band. The buttstock was of an odd combless design, with a slightly crescent-shaped butt plate. A wooden handguard extended from the receiver ring to the upper band. The stock and handguard were held to the barrel by two bands, a wide two-strap upper band with a bayonet stud and a stacking swivel, and an oval lower band which carried the upper sling swivel. The lower swivel was on the lower edge of the stock in front of the toe. The action was a modified Mauser design, with twin opposed locking lugs at the front end of the bolt, and the long elastic extractor typical of Mauser actions. The bolt handle was a peculiar design, being bent back and down; the bolt handle knob had a large hole drilled in it for lightness.

A blade front sight, protected by heavy sight wings, was mounted on a band near the muzzle. The rear sights, though made without any provision for windage, were splendidly suited for combat use. They were mounted right back on the receiver bridge, where rifle sights should be. They are known as aperture or peep sights, a type which was long neglected for general military use. The shooter sights through a circular hole in the sight slide, and since the hole is so close to his eye, the novice marksman is astonished to find that he sees not only the front sight and the target, but a large portion of the surrounding landscape as well, and will doubtless complain that the sight is not fine enough. The sight works on the principle that the human eye automatically seeks out the optical center of the aperture since that portion admits more light than the edges. It is easy to pick up the target, even a moving one, through these sights, and one is hardly aware of the rear sight's existence; there is no conscious effort involved. With other rifle sights, the shooter has to try to focus his eyes on a rear sight about a foot ahead of his eyes, a front sight a couple of feet ahead of that, and a target several hundred yards ahead of that. The eye cannot do it. It shifts focus rapidly between the three objects. The shooter soon finds that he can hit a target whether or not its image is in focus; the front sight is the thing to watch, since a front sight placed to one side of the target causes the rifle to fire away from the target at an angle governed by the displacement of the front sight. The aperture rear sight, by appearing as a blur to the shooter's eye, allows him to concentrate on the front sight. The Enfield rear sight, adjustable for ranges between 200 and 1600 yards, was protected by two large vertical sight wings.

The rifle operated much like the Springfield, except that the bolt cocked on the forward or closing thrust, instead of the opening movement, a feature which was quite popular in Great Britain and greatly disliked in the United States. Actually, it's a fielder's choice. The British action gives slightly easier extraction as the rifle heats up, while the American rifles give much smoother overall operation.

The Enfield was loaded by turning the bolt handle to the left and pulling it rearward, inserting a clip of five cartridges into the slots in the receiver bridge, and stripping them off the clip into the magazine. The deep-bellied Enfield magazine held six cartridges and could be so loaded if necessary. The rifle operates as follows. Suppose a cartridge has just been fired. By raising the bolt handle, one turns the bolt to the left. Since the cocking piece lug is held by a groove in the receiver, it is forced straight to the rear in the bolt and catches in the half cock notch. This action serves to withdraw the striker back into the bolt face. As the locking lugs clear their recesses, they cam the bolt slightly to the rear, providing slow initial extraction. While the bolt rotates, the extractor is prevented from turning by grooves in the receiver which hold it immobile.

The ninety-degree turn of the bolt places the locking lugs in a horizontal position and the bolt is free to be drawn straight to the rear, the extractor continuing to pull the empty case out of the chamber. As the slotted left hand locking lug reaches the ejector, the latter rides into the slot and as the bolt continues rearward, it strikes the rear of the cartridge which is forced to pivot about the extractor and is thrown clear of the rifle. Just prior to ejection, the bolt has moved back far enough to allow the top cartridge in the magazine to rise up, under pressure of the magazine spring, into the return path of the lower left edge of the bolt.

Forward movement of the bolt pushes the top cartridge over the feed ramp; the extractor claw engages the extracting groove in the cartridge case. As the bolt continues forward, the sear notch in the cocking piece engages the sear nose and is held by it. The bolt, still moving forward, slides over the striker, further compressing the mainspring. Rotation of the bolt handle to the right engages the locking lugs in their cam shaped recesses, which forces the bolt home, seating the cartridge and completing compression of the mainspring. When the trigger is pulled, it first bears against the receiver, depressing the sear nose and taking up the slack in the trigger pull. Then the heel of the trigger engages the receiver and pulls the sear nose completely away from the notch in the cocking piece. The striker, under the released power of the compressed mainspring, is driven forward, strikes the primer, and detonates it.

The American Enfield was chambered for the same ammunition as the

Model 1903 Springfield, a brass bottlenecked cartridge case, loaded with between forty-five and fifty grains of perforated cylindrical grains of pyrocellulose. The bullet, weighing one hundred and fifty grains, was made of a lead core covered by a cupronickel jacket. As the war started, the cartridge was primed by a mixture of tersulphide of antimony, potassium chlorate, and sulphur; in 1917 this was changed to omit the sulphur and substitute lead sulphocyanide.

The Enfield, while no thing of beauty, with its deep belly and awkward lines, was one of the best rifles of World War I. As stated before, its battle sights were excellently suited for the purpose, and its nickel steel action is one of the strongest ever made. Over two million Enfields were produced during World War I by private contractors. It was the rifle with which most of our troops were armed in World War I, and was dragged out of storage to serve in World War II.

Footnote to History

IN any discussion of military weapons, it is tempting, but profitless, to treat the firearm as a separate entity, and consider its effect upon the wars in which it was used in purely physical terms, as though chamber pressure, velocity, muzzle energy, and ballistic coefficients represent the sum total of what it can do. On the battlefield, the rifle represents the limit to which a nation's identity and strength have been advanced. It stands between its masters and defeat. How it got there and how it performed can be understood only through a necessary digression into the times and circumstances which thrust it into that position.

The country found that the end of the Civil War confronted it with two large-scale military problems, in addition to the necessity for military occupation of the South. The first was of Mexican origin and was solved, rather neatly, before serious trouble developed. It all began in 1855, when two Indians were in control of the Mexican Government, Juan Alverez, the president, and Benito Juarez, his Minister of Justice. Both uncompromising men, they passed a series of restrictive laws which struck at the core of every group in Mexico, the army, the Church, and the great landowners' corporations. They succeeded in alienating themselves from everyone in power, and faced with an impossible situation, Alverez returned to his mountain farmlands, after two months in office. The safest place, too, for the laws against the Church inspired a clerical rebellion which was not quelled until 1857. During this time a reform Constitution was in the making, validating in its basic tenets the laws suggested by Juarez. Its adoption, encompassing unalterable restrictions against the groups originally made angry by Juarez's laws, brought about a total rupture between Church and State. Another rebellion. Juarez ran *his* government from Vera Cruz, borrowing money from France to keep the wheels turning; the conservative forces, backed by the landowners and the Church, ran *theirs* from Mexico City, during the course of a Civil War which lasted three years. Inflexible old Juarez regained control in 1861, the same year that the United States was split by civil war. The time factor is important. With the United States no longer able to enforce the Monroe Doctrine, and Mexico ripe for picking, Napoleon III of France figured it high time to take over Mexico as payment for the debt. After bitter fighting on the Atlantic Coast, he succeeded, and a Hapsburg Prince, Maximilian, was placed in office as ostensible ruler of Mexico. He didn't stand a chance, for Napoleon became an unwelcome benefactor. What the Church lost would stay lost, and the conservatives were to stay out of power. Poor Maximilian, trying with obvious sincerity to be a good ruler, was regarded by the conservatives as too liberal and by the liberals as too conservative. The liberals had no intention of giving up, Napoleon or no Napoleon, and fighting continued to lay its whiplash of pain across the length and breadth of the country. At last, in 1865, the monarchists were in virtual control of Mexico; Juarez alone resisted them. In 1865—the same year that General Lee surrendered at Appomattox courthouse. With the celerity of thought, tons of arms and ammunition were smuggled across the border, and the ranks of Juarez's flagging army were growing with both Union and Confederate veterans; fighting flared up again. Such were the circumstances when the United States, at that time unquestionably the strongest military power in the world, turned a baleful eye on the whole subject of Napoleonic intervention in Mexico; it was suggested to the French Government that part of the Army, in need of rest and sunshine, might be furloughed south for a vacation in the tropics. Napoleon was no fool. Germany was even more unfriendly to France than usual and a double war would be disastrous. He pulled out, leaving Maximilian to be thrown to the lions. Maximilian was subsequently put before a firing squad, and the United States won its war with France before it got started.

The other problem concerned the American Indian and was not to be solved so easily. It had several aspects that were not generally realized at the time. The Indians had been shoved westward about as far as they could go. They were running out of territory. In so doing, they tended to consolidate, and the vast plains tribes were united in one purpose, to resist any more territorial encroachment. The Indians were being armed by civilian agencies, and usually procured the breech-loading magazine rifles that the Army couldn't afford or wouldn't adopt. Often the Indians were better armed than the troops they fought, something of tremendous importance when the rifle was the main fighting tool.

As if to compound the error, the Army, in relation to the size of the job it had to perform, was at its lowest ebb in history. Its total strength was reduced to somewhere under forty thousand troops, parts of which, such as heavy artillery and the occupation troops of the South, were automatically unable to fight on the frontier. A fractional part of the Army was assigned the duty of protecting settlers, railroads, and isolated towns against hundreds of thousands of hostile tribesmen, across an area which could comfortably hold all of Europe. As more and more settlers streamed westward, there were fights of increasing size and severity, and the Army was always handed a question with a choice of two wrong answers. If it failed to whip the Indians, no matter what the circumstances, it was subject to Congressional investigation; if it did a really thorough job, it was roundly damned in the tabloids for exterminating innocent people. Actually, the record of all sides was a bad one. Everyone, the Army, the Indians, the white settlers, and the Indian agents, lied, cheated, and broke treaties, and in turn were subjected to the same treatment.

The most famous of all the Indian battles, though, oddly enough, a non-decisive one, was a slashing defeat suffered by the Army at the hands of the Sioux, whose dying gasp of power resulted in the annihilation of George Custer's tiny force at the Little Big Horn. That was too much. The Army mustered what strength it had and, while never destroying the Sioux, did scatter them, and effectively ended the threat of the plains Indians. There was hardly time for a breather before some spectacular bungling by the White Man gave the Army the same job to do all over again, first with the Nez Percé Indians in the northwest and later against the Apaches, the world's finest light cavalry, in the southwest. The Indian Wars did not actually end until the 1890's, a time within the life span of millions of people living today.

The fact that the United States is protected by several thousand miles of open water on either flank has proved to be a mixed blessing. It has not saved us from seven wars with foreign powers, including several invasions, in less than one hundred and eighty years; yet it has given us a bogus sense of security which has often blinded us to the probability that in this world another war is usually around the corner. Both the Spanish-American War and World War I tell the same distressing story, which follows a plot as rigid and stylized as a Chinese ritual play. The tendency has been, at the conclusion of a war, to dismember the armed forces, cut appropriations to pieces, reduce promotions, stultify initiative, maneuver the Services into a fight with a major power and then wonder why the Army could not, overnight, meet its combat requirements efficiently. So far luck has been with us. In the Spanish-American War we were fortunate enough to have a rather weak opponent, and in World War I our enemy had taken on every major power in Europe all by itself before we entered into the conflict.

The Spanish American War proved the absolute necessity for employing smokeless powder in both small arms and artillery, but that was obvious before the war; the Army was getting around to it when war struck, and the need was no great surprise to anyone. The major postwar changes were those of organization; service schools were reorganized, a staff college was established to tie every branch of service together, and for the first time we had a functioning general staff and the realization that, if we didn't have a large Army, it had to be one capable of acting as a cadre, to expand rapidly in case of a war. Those were postwar changes; the war which made them overwhelmingly necessary was a debacle. The Army, resigned to a diet of short rations since the end of the Civil War, could not be expected to suddenly multiply like a colony of protozoans without some dreadful growing pains. The ports of embarkation in Florida resembled hobo jungles, where disease almost halted operations before they began. The supply handling was a preview to Gallipoli, there being nothing really unusual in sending the troops to one point and their ammunition to another. The .45-70 rifle made a dismal showing against the Spanish Mauser, and the smoke it produced when fired could usually be counted on to bring down a stinging rain of jacketed bullets; our artillery, which fired black powder, was no better off. The Krag-Jörgensen, our new smokeless powder magazine rifle, was good enough, but there were too few to go around. The infantry, miserably ill-

equipped for tropical duty, floundered around the jungle for several weeks before reaching attack positions before the hills overlooking Santiago, winning their objectives after charging headlong through murderous fire from covered positions. But the Cuban campaign was primarily a naval show, and ended when Admiral Cevera steamed out of Santiago harbor and took a terrible pasting from the American fleet.

The Spanish Navy took another thumping in the Philippines, and the conquest of the Spanish Army there proved to be no great problem; but conquering the natives was something else again. The Army, which was getting the standard post-war-apathy routine from the Government, had to subjugate some extremely wily guerilla fighters, civilians one moment, soldiers the next, one of the nastiest jobs to which an organized Army can be assigned. It took about three years of straight jungle fighting, after which the Army went into its usual peacetime slump.

It was, rather fortunately, forced into large scale mobilization on the Mexican border by Pancho Villa's raids shortly before we entered into World War I, and was in somewhat better shape for rapid expansion than it would have been without the shock of necessity to alert the country.

World War I came about just after magazine rifles, machine guns, and artillery had been brought to an extremely high state of development. These weapons, intended to win wars, very nearly outsmarted themselves by turning the war into almost indefinite prolongation, by stalemating the fighting. They did so by raining so much metal into the front lines that maneuver and indeed, bare movement, became almost impossible. The use of dug-in emplacements and thousands of miles of barbed wire, a device originally intended to fence in cattle, became standard all along the lines, so that the entire front became almost immobile. No one Army had the concentrated power to break through the front, which consisted of row after row of trenches, set in a depth of several miles. A force which broke through the first line soon ran smack into another, and still another; and offensives, great exhausting shattering drives, usually bogged down from sheer inanition after expending thousands of men to win a few miles of mud, churned into a nightmare lunar surface by uncounted rounds of artillery fire. The tank, though obviously a weapon of great promise, was a balky unpredictable machine whose mechanical failings and limited number obviated its chances of accomplishing what it might well have done, break the suffocating deadlock between the two lines.

The war was ended by the appearance of over one million United States troops, in whose very freshness lay the new strength for one monster push against the German lines. But the American divisions were blooded when the Allies were on the taking, not the giving, end of the war. As United States soldiers began to reach France in greater and greater numbers, the German high command realized the submarine had failed to isolate the United States from Europe, and Hindenburg and Ludendorff were called upon to do something, and do it fast. Their answer was to order one thundering drive against the British 5th Army, which was flattened by the advance. The Germans made a thirty-mile advance before they were halted. Not success, but close to it. In the spring of 1918 they tried again, this time across the Aisne River, a drive whose success was almost its undoing. The trough of liquid mud which formed the battlefield prevented the artillery from keeping up with its own infantry, and the drive ground to a halt at the Marne River. Before it began anew, the American 2nd and 3rd divisions were moved to the banks of the Marne, in the area of Chateau Thierry, and the German offensive ran afoul of fresh troops and a really good group of riflemen. The attack died after a week of the most deadly fighting, and German strength began to recede from this, its high water mark. Thereafter, the end was in sight.

In a sense, World War I was the Civil War all over again, though for different reasons. The power of firearms had once again outrun tactics and methods of transportation. In the Civil War, frontal assaults were made against direct fire from dug-in positions because commanders did not know what else to do. In World War I, the front stretched across the width of Europe; flanking movements were impossible. There was simply no flank, and frontal assaults were made because there was nothing else to do. In either case, the results were equally hideous.

The infantry had outgrown their age-old function of spear carriers; the magazine rifle, whose striking power has not improved materially since World War I, could methodically chop an assault to pieces. The emphasis on development since that date has been directed, not in improving the striking power of the rifle, but in increasing its rate of fire, the results of which bring us up to the most modern rifles of today.

U.S. Rifle, Caliber .30, M1

IN the spring of 1903, when the United States Army was still testing a bolt action rifle which was later to be known as the Model 1903, Ordnance took cognizance of the developmental step that was really taking place. The irresistible trend towards increased rapidity of fire had caused the adoption of the Krag-Jörgensen magazine rifle and was producing the clip-loaded Model 1903. What the hell, figured the Army, the next step is only a matter of time. In the 1903 annual report to the Secretary of War, by the Chief of Ordnance, the section devoted to small arms ended with this statement. "The Department is encouraging inventors who approach it upon the subject of the production of an automatic musket, as it seems that the principle—being in line of the reduction of the interval between aimed shots—follows the course which led to the introduction of the magazine rifle, and has therefore at least sufficient promise of value to be worthy of attention to the degree necessary to advance the question from a mechanical to a military one." This, remember, was before the manufacture of the Model 1903 Springfield had even begun. It turned out to be a long search, culminating in 1936 with the adoption of the M1 rifle. United States Ordnance was among the first organizations to foresee the full capabilities of the semiautomatic rifle, and at the start of World War II, the United States and Russia were the only nations so armed.

Automatic or semiautomatic firearms are, by definition, those firearms which utilize the power of the exploding cartridge to extract and eject the spent round, and cock and reload themselves without any manual effort on the part of the shooters. The true automatic weapon is one which continues to fire uninterruptedly as long as pressure is maintained on the trigger, machine guns and submachine guns falling into this class. The semiautomatic weapon, which was what the Army was referring to with its quaint cognomen of automatic musket, is a firearm which performs its cycle of operation automatically, but with a mechanical interruption just prior to firing. There has been a contradiction in terms because several classes of firearms, notably the so-called automatic pistols and automatic shotguns, are actually semiautomatic in operation. The Germans cleared up the misunderstanding, in their own country at any rate, by referring to semiautomatic weapons as *selbstladers,* or self-loaders. The terms will probably become more rather than less interchangeable, due to the present trend to design shoulder arms capable of firing either automatically or semiautomatically.

Be that as it may, the automatic and semiautomatic arms are not recent developments. Pistols operating on such principles were in use prior to 1900. The machine gun, which also used the waste power of the cartridge to achieve rapid fire, was invented in the early 1890's. The first workable semiautomatic military rifle was designed in Mexico in 1904 by General Mondragon, and adopted by the Mexican Government in 1911. The actual manufacture was done at Neuhausen in Switzerland, and at the outbreak of war in 1914, the entire output of the plant was diverted to Germany. The Mondragon saw limited action in that war before being discarded as unreliable in combat. The French also produced a semiautomatic rifle, the Model 1917, known as the St. Etienne, a doomed marriage of bad design and rather sloppy manufacture. It too failed to produce any rave notices, and the only automatic weapons used in that war were the automatic pistol and the machine gun, which dominated the battlefield. The United States manufactured, in great secrecy, a gadget intended to convert every Springfield rifle into a submachine gun. Though made by the tens of thousands, the device never saw action, due to the rapid and unexpected collapse of the German armed forces, and its battle efficiency remains a moot point. To insure secrecy, it was deliberately misnamed, Automatic Pistol, Caliber .30, Model of 1918. Today it is usually called the Pederson Device, after Mr. J. D. Pederson, its inventor. In essence, the Pederson Device was a sort of self-contained firing unit inserted in the rifle in place of the regular bolt. A forty-round box magazine sloped up from the right side of the device, giving it a tremendous magazine capacity of caliber .30 cartridges, each roughly the same size of the .32 automatic pistol round. After World War I most of the Pederson Devices were destroyed to prevent every civilian-owned Springfield from becoming a potential submachine gun. Interesting gadget, the Pederson; the military point is . . . would it have worked? It had a number of disadvantages, and after extensive post-war testing, it was rejected by the Army. It fired a notoriously weak cartridge, weaker, in fact, than the present-day carbine cartridge, which is no great shakes in range, penetration, or ability as a manstopper. Its use would have required the foot soldier to carry two bolts, two supplies of ammunition, both in clips and magazines, and various accessories. Alone, the factor of added weight would probably evoke nothing but caustic laughter from troops who carry BAR's machine guns, and mortars around the battlefield; but the presence and complexity and the possibility of loss of all that gear dangling from one's cartridge belt would pose a more serious problem. It has been pointed out that the Pederson round produced no ballistic crack as it passed overhead, in contrast to the Springfield, whose fire creates as murderous and malevolent a sound as one shall ever hear. As such, it was concluded that the Springfield created more fear in the enemy by virtue of the awesome noise it made as it passed by. Admittedly, its sound does inspire a fervent desire to be elsewhere, anywhere. But it is this writer's opinion that the morale of the infantryman, who is daily subjected to machine gun fire, artillery and mortar fire, bombing, strafing, and huge tanks of jellied gasoline, will show no improvement if he fails to hear small arms noise. The Pederson Device was the result of sound design and concept, but its solution to the firepower question has since been superseded by better weapons.

Anyway, the early 1920's saw no nation armed with a semiautomatic rifle. The United States, however, was engaged in a very determined search for a suitable one. Experimental rifles came and went, among them some very ingenious designs. But the kettle did not come to a boil until 1928, when Mr. Garand began work on a gas-operated rifle, chambered for the .276 Pederson rifle cartridge, which at that time was generally supposed to replace caliber .30 ammunition. As the result of tests conducted in 1929, the Garand rifle was issued for field trials in extremely limited number. It proved to be a splendid rifle and after being converted to use caliber .30 ammunition, was adopted by the United States armed forces in 1936.

This rifle, called the M1, bears a strong resemblance, in general concept, to the old Mondragon design. Part of the gas which drives the bullet forward is allowed to escape through a hole drilled through the underside of the barrel near the muzzle. It flows into a small chamber, the rear portion of which is blocked by a piston head. The trapped gas impinges against the piston which extends the entire length of the barrel and is connected with the bolt. The piston moves rearward, unlocking the bolt, which extracts and ejects the spent cartridge case, and cocks the hammer. As the bolt reaches its rearmost position, a powerful return spring, compressed by the piston's rearward trip, forces the bolt forward; in so doing, the bolt picks up a fresh cartridge from the magazine and seats and locks it in the chamber. All this takes place in a fraction of a second, so that the moving parts are seen only as a blur to the naked eye.

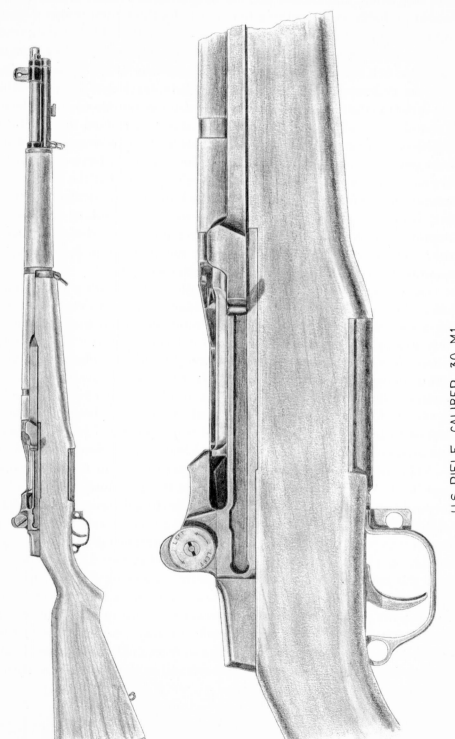

U.S. RIFLE, CALIBER .30, M1

The rifle is 43 inches long and weighs about nine and a half pounds, without sling or bayonet. The barrel, 24 inches long, is rifled with four grooves which make one turn to the right in 10 inches. The 29.75-inch pistol grip stock extends to the upper sling swivel. Above it is a wooden handguard and in front of it an upper handguard which covers the barrel and operating rod and piston from the upper sling swivel to the rear of the gas cylinder. The upper sling swivel is mounted on the underside of the stock ferrule, a U-shaped metal bracket at the front of the stock, designed to hold the upper handguard in place. The lower swivel is attached to the buttstock just in front of the toe. The blade front sight, protected by heavy wings, is on the top of the gas cylinder tube assembly. The rear sights are of the aperture type, set on a gear rack stem on the rear of the receiver, and can be adjusted for elevation and windage by means of elevation and windage knobs on the left and right of the sight base. It is graduated for ranges between 100 and 1200 yards. Each click on the sights moves the impact of the bullet through one minute of angle, whether the adjustment be for elevation or windage. When fired at a vertical target, each click corresponds to a change of one inch on the target for every hundred yards of range. Thus, one click moves the strike of the bullet one inch at 100 yards, 2 inches at 200 yards, and so on.

About four years after adoption, the M1 was modified slightly. The gas cylinder tube, originally screwed onto the barrel, was slipped over the barrel in a set of splines, and was held in place by a gas cylinder lock and a lock plug threaded into the gas cylinder tube. The front sight wings were bent outward; and a stamped trigger guard replaced the original machined guard. Lately, most of the gas cylinder plugs have been replaced by plugs enabling any rifle so equipped to fire rifle grenades in the new grenade launchers. But by and large there have been no important changes. The latest modifications have produced an entirely new rifle, which will be treated later.

The M1 rifle is loaded by pulling back the bolt manually until it locks into its open position. A clip of eight cartridges is shoved vertically downward onto the magazine follower. Complete loading releases the bolt, which slides forward, picks the top cartridge out of the magazine, and seats it in the chamber. The cartridges are loaded *en bloc*, that is, cartridges and clip together are inserted into the magazine, which depends on a clip for its functioning. When the last round has been fired, the empty clip is automatically ejected from the rifle, and the bolt is held back in its open position. The safety is mounted in the trigger guard, in front of the trigger. When

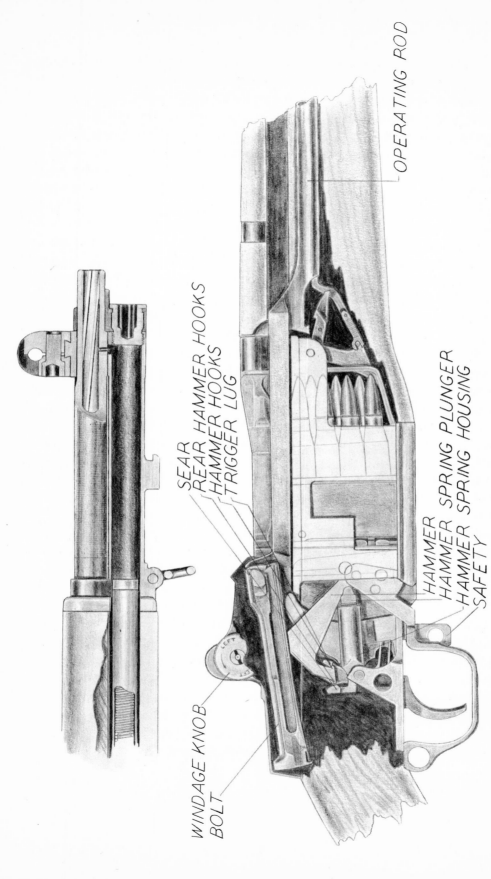

SHIELDS

OPERATING ROD

SEAR
REAR HAMMER HOOKS
HAMMER HOOKS
TRIGGER LUG

HAMMER
HAMMER SPRING PLUNGER
HAMMER SPRING HOUSING
SAFETY

WINDAGE KNOB
BOLT

SECTIONAL VIEW OF M1 RIFLE, WITH BOLT IN REARMOST POSITION

locked, the safety protrudes into the guard itself. It is unlocked by pushing it forward out of the guard.

When the rifle is loaded and the bolt is closed, the cocked hammer is held against the tension of its compressed spring by engagement of the hammer hooks with the trigger lugs. Pressing the trigger disengages the hooks from the lugs and the hammer swings forward and strikes the firing pin which in turn hits the cartridge primer. The explosion drives the bullet down the barrel and as it passes the gas port near the muzzle, part of the compressed gas escapes into the cylinder beneath it, drives the operating rod rearward and begins to compress the coil spring within it.

The initial rearward movement of the operating rod is independent of the bolt. After five sixteenths of an inch the cam surface in the hump of the operating rod reaches the right hand lug on the bolt, camming it counterclockwise and unlocking it. The five sixteenths inch delay allows the bullet to clear the muzzle and lets gas pressure drop to safe limits before the bolt is opened. The rotation of the bolt serves the fourfold purpose of unlocking withdrawal of the firing pin inside the bolt face, camming the hammer away from the firing pin, and providing slow initial extraction. Continued rearward movement of the operating rod carries the bolt straight to the rear, causing the extractor claw to pull the empty case clear of the chamber. As soon as it does clear, the ejector, which maintains constant pressure against the case, flips it clear of the rifle. The rear end of the bolt pivots the hammer backwards and rides over it, compressing the hammer spring, and comes to rest when its lugs hit the receiver bridge. The rearward motion of the bolt exposes the magazine, whose follower spring forces a new round into the return path of the bolt.

The operating rod spring, compressed inside the operating rod by its rearward trip, begins to expand, carrying the bolt forward and picking up the top cartridge. The hammer, which was held down by the bottom of the bolt, attempts to ride forward, but is held by engagement between the trigger lugs and the hammer hooks, if the trigger has been released. If the trigger is still held back, the hammer hooks will be held by the sear. Releasing the trigger will disengage the sear and the trigger lugs will catch the hammer and hold it. Thus, whether or not the trigger is held back, the hammer is positively held, allowing only one shot per squeeze of the trigger.

As the bolt nears its forward position, the extractor slips into the cannelure in the cartridge, a movement which also serves to compress the ejector spring. The operating, or right hand, lug on the bolt is cammed clockwise by the rear cam surface in the hump of the operating rod. The bolt lugs, turned into their recesses, lock the action, and the operating rod continues forward for its five sixteenths of an inch. The rifle is now ready to be fired again. The process continues, with each shot, until the last round is ejected. When the rifle is empty the empty clip is ejected from the magazine and the bolt remains in its open position for fast reloading.

Quite a step forward beyond earlier weapons; in fact the M1 contains many features considered undesirable in the past. It can shoot fast enough to set fire to the stock; it is of complex design, is expensive to manufacture, requires a lot of care, and is without a doubt the finest military rifle ever put into production.

It is far from perfect; it has to be so. Any piece of machinery represents a practical balance between an almost infinite number of divergent factors. The resulting compromise will of necessity, be deficient in the extreme perfection of any given factor. The military rifle is something like a decathlon athlete, who can easily be beaten by experts in any of the fields in which he competes. But he can do all of them better than any of the experts. So far, the M1 has won the military decathlon hands down.

The standard ammunition for the M1 rifle is of the same size and power So can machine guns, pistols, and just about every weapon used in combat today. Troops armed with it can run out of ammunition, just as troops armed with throwing spears or large rocks have run out of ammunition. In battle, that will happen as inevitably as night follows day. The only valid question is whether its increased rapidity of fire justifies its increased ammunition expenditure, its vulnerability to jamming by dirt, its high manufacturing cost. As if in answer, our next service rifle is going to fire even faster.

The standard ammunition for the M1 rifle is of the same size and power as that used in the Springfield and Enfield rifles. The drawn brass cartridge case consists of a conical body joined to the cylindrical neck by a sharper cone, called the shoulder. It is the familiar bottlenecked .30-06 design. The case is entirely rimless, having an extracting groove cut about the circumference of the case. The cartridge is manufactured with several types of bullets, depending on the use to which the round will be put.

Normal issue is called ball ammunition. The bullet consists of two parts, a gilding metal jacket or a steel jacket coated with gilding metal, and a core of lead-antimony alloy. The complete bullet, shaped into a double arc point and a flat base, weighs one hundred and fifty-two grains. It is loaded into the case in front of fifty grains of smokeless powder, producing a chamber pressure of fifty thousand pounds per square inch. Muzzle velocity is 2800 ft/sec.

Another round issued out in tremendous quantity is the armor piercing cartridge. Its bullet is made of a gilding metal jacket and a core of tungsten-chrome steel or manganese-molybdenum steel. The space between the core and the jacket is filled with lead. It weighs either one hundred and sixty-eight and five-tenths or one hundred and sixty-six grains, depending on the core material. The fifty-three grain powder charge produces a chamber pressure of fifty thousand pounds per square inch and a muzzle velocity of 2,770 ft/sec. Armor piercing ammunition is readily identified by the bullet-tip coated with black paint.

A third type, sometimes employed in rifles, is tracer ammunition. The bullet is made of a gilding metal or gilding metal-clad steel jacket, a lead-antimony point filler, and a base filler of igniter and tracer compound. The bullet weighs either one hundred and fifty-two and five-tenths or one hundred and forty-three and five-tenths grains, depending on whether steel or gilding metal is used to form the jacket. The gilding metal jacketed bullet leaves the muzzle at 2750 ft/sec; the other bullet's muzzle velocity is 2710 ft/sec. Tracer ammunition is identified by a bullet-tip coated with red or orange paint. The tracer compound will burn, with intense brilliance and heat, for the length of time it takes the bullet to travel about 1000 yards. One of the tracer bullet's uses is its incendiary effect and as such is extremely dangerous to fire into timber, brush, or grass. Civilian shooters shouldn't bother with it anyway; it is hard on rifle barrels and is fairly inaccurate, due to the fact that it changes both its weight and its center of balance while in flight. The spread of its shot groups is more than twice that of the other ammunition.

There are two other types of ammunition commonly fired through the M1 rifle, grenade and blank cartridges. The grenade cartridge has no bullet; the case is closed at the mouth by a series of five crimps. It is loaded with five grains of black powder and forty grains of smokeless powder, and is used only to jolt a rifle grenade into motion by gas pressure alone. The blank cartridge, of course, has no bullet either, and to keep the powder in, has a paper wad crimped into the case mouth. Blank or not, it is extremely dangerous up to about 20 feet. The wad can kill at close range. Failing that, it can provide the victim with a tremendous collection of powder burns.

Four other types of caliber .30 ammunition can be fired through the M1, although all but one are designed primarily for machine gun use. There is the incendiary cartridge, identified by a blue-tipped bullet. It leaves no trace while in flight, but the nose and core of the bullet are filled by an incendiary compound which ignites upon impact. The second is a combination armor piercing and incendiary bullet, a standard AP bullet with an incendiary compound in place of the lead nose filler. The tip of the bullet is coated with aluminum paint. The third machine gun round is frangible ammunition. The bullet tip is painted green with a white annulus to the rear. The bullet itself is made of a half and half mixture of powdered lead and bakelite. It is designed to be fired directly at target planes and disintegrates upon impact with three sixteenths of an inch metal airplane skin.

The last type of ammunition should be avoided at all costs. It is test ammunition, used for proof firing barrels and finished rifles. It develops a chamber pressure of seventy thousand pounds per square inch, and is fired at the arsenals only when the gun is behind metal shielding. The entire cartridge case is tin plated to identify it.

Most of the service rounds commonly fired in the M1 use the same propellant, a single base powder known as IMR (improved military rifle). It is straight nitrocellulose, coated with a deterrent and glazed with graphite. It contains a small amount of potassium salts to reduce flash and is made in the form of short monoperforated cylindrical grains.

U.S. Rifles, Caliber .30, M1C and M1D

BOTH the M1C and M1D rifles are standard M1 rifles modified for use by snipers by the addition of telescopic sights, lace-on cheek pads, and flash hiders. Since a cartridge clip is mandatory in the functioning of an M1 rifle, the telescope is in a mount which is offset to the left in order to allow clip loading. The telescopes themselves are usually commercial hunting sights, such as the Lyman Alaskan or other big game sights. The only difference between the M1C and M1D is that the former was made from completed rifles. The M1D cannot be made from previously manufactured weapons because the scope mount is attached to metal ordinarily removed in manufacture.

U.S. Carbine, Caliber .30,
M1, M1A1, and M2

UP to this point the writer has made virtually no mention of the various United States military carbines or the early musketoons, thereby treating them, in a sense, as though they didn't exist. The reason is that the book covers only those shoulder arms carried by foot troops. Up until World War I, the carbine was a specialized weapon issued to mounted units, such as cavalry and artillery, units whose jobs were made easier if the men were unencumbered by a long rifle or musket. The normal carbine was built by the same machinery as any rifle of the same model, and was a carbine by virtue of its short barrel, cut-down stock, and the fact that ordinarily it had no provision for attaching a bayonet. Usually, any given carbine used ammunition of slightly less power than a rifle of the same model to compensate for the carbine's lessened weight and length; however the cartridge case was the same for both arms.

The last carbine of this type was manufactured on the Krag-Jörgensen action, the Spanish-American War service arm. The invention of decent smokeless powder and its accompanying improvement in the ballistic properties of propellants at the turn of the century made it possible to do away with a carbine of any kind. The Model 1903 rifle had a 24-inch barrel and was suitable for issue to all arms of the service.

By the time World War II was under way, the infantry was armed with large numbers of weapons and equipment which required a crew of several men for their operation, machine guns, mortars, rocket launchers, anti-tank guns, radios, and so on. A full size rifle was just unnecessary weight for such troops, and the service pistol, while quite powerful, lacked the range for any but the closest kind of self defense. The M1 carbine was designd to arm these men with a light, short, compact semiautomatic rifle. However, service ammunition and a short barreled five-pound rifle makes an ugly blast and recoil combination, plus an impossible designing problem. Accordingly, the carbine, while bored to caliber .30, fires a cartridge both smaller and considerably weaker than the standard caliber .30 ammunition.

If total replacement of the pistol was the goal of the carbine issue, it was a failure. There are still upwards of twenty-seven hundred pistols in every infantry division. Machine gunners, mortarmen, tankers, various staff members, and thousands of others still carry the pistol. What the carbine did was form a handy shoulder weapon for *some* of the men who formerly carried pistols. Even so, the carbine is issued out in numbers which are undoubtedly beyond the expectations of those responsible for its issue. Over seventy-four hundred men in each infantry division are armed with the carbine, give or take a hundred or so, according to whatever the varying Table of Organization and Equipment calls for.

The reduced power of the carbine allowed it to be built on a design which at the time was not considered feasible with the M1 rifle ammunition. Though the overall operation of both shoulder arms is very similar, and it is common to think of the carbine as a baby M1, the carbine differs from the rifle in several general features. In the rifle, the gases are tapped off near the muzzle, necessitating the use of a long continuous piston; in the carbine, the burning powder gases are allowed to escape a short distance ahead of the chamber. This makes possible a much shorter operating rod, and does away with the wooden handguard that covers it, and the gas cylinder arrangement near the muzzle. The M1 rifle feeds through a clip, while the carbine uses a sheet metal box magazine, much the same as that on an automatic pistol. Lastly, the two trigger mechanisms are designed quite differently. The reduction of power in the carbine cartridge allows the use of much smaller parts, producing a weight reduction of over four pounds, and a 10-inch difference in over-all length.

The basic carbine, which has a one piece walnut stock and a wooden handguard covering the rear part of the barrel, is practically a diminutive copy of the M1 rifle receiver, and the bolt, operating rod, and lockwork are but slightly modified versions of the rifle action. A caliber .30 round barrel, a shade under 18 inches long and rifled with four grooves, is threaded into the receiver. It has a blade front sight protected by metal wings, on a band near the muzzle. The rear sight is one of two types. The earliest carbine sights were L-shaped, consisting of two arms at right angles, each pierced by an aperture. A flat spring retained the sight leaf in either position. The two apertures were set for ranges of 150 and 300 yards, and one of the two arms was always vertical, interpolation being necessary for any other range. There were no provisions for windage adjustment. A later design,

SHIELDS

U.S. CARBINE, CAL. .30, M1

U.S. CARBINE CAL. .30, M1A1

U.S. CARBINE CAL. .30, M2

also mounted at the rear of the receiver, consisted of a sliding ramp design which was graduated in 50 yard increments from 100 to 300 yards. A windage knob allowed lateral adjustment of the sight aperture to the right and left of center. The front end of the stock and the handguard are held to the barrel by a band which carries the upper sling swivel, mounted on the left side of the stock. The lower end of the sling is looped around a metal oiler located in a slot cut through the buttstock. This arrangement, often found on foreign rifles, allows the carbine to be carried flat against the soldier's back, and keeps the trigger guard and protruding magazine comfortably out of the way.

A sheet metal box magazine, carrying fifteen cartridges in a vertical, double-staggered column, protrudes from the stock just forward of the trigger guard. The safety is a small lever located immediately in front of the trigger on the right side of the guard. In front of it is a metal push-through catch which releases the magazine.

The carbine is loaded by inserting a loaded magazine through the bottom of the magazine well and pushing it upward until the magazine catch clicks into place. To insure this, it is best to load the carbine with the bolt held open. When the bolt is manually released it snaps forward, carrying the top round from the magazine into the chamber and locking it there. The weapon is now loaded, with the cocked hammer held back by engagement of the sear with a sear notch in the hammer. Pressing the trigger releases the hammer, allowing it to swing forward under the impress of the hammer spring, striking the rear tang of the firing pin, which transmits the blow to the cartridge primer. The cartridge explodes, driving the bullet down the barrel. As the bullet passes the gas port, a small hole drilled in the underside of the barrel, some of the powder gases pass through the port into the cylinder and impinge sharply against a piston head at the rear of the cylinder. After the piston has moved about three-sixteenths of an inch it is stopped, the blow being transmitted to the weighted operating slide, driving it to the rear. The operating slide moves to the rear about five-sixteenths of an inch before a cam recess in the slide engages the right hand lug on the bolt. During this time the bullet has left the barrel and pressure has dropped sufficiently to allow the action to be opened. The operating slide continues rearward, rotating the bolt out of its locked position and then carrying it straight to the rear. The extractor, mounted on the front end of the bolt, pulls the empty case out of the chamber as the bolt begins to rotate and, in standard bolt action fashion, withdraws the firing pin within the bolt face and backs the hammer away from the rear of the firing pin. Continued rearward motion of the operating slide pulls the bolt straight to the rear, extracting and ejecting the empty case and cocking the hammer backwards, compressing its spring and causing it to be held by the sear. The magazine, meanwhile, has popped another live cartridge into the return path of the bolt. The rearward movement of the slide is stopped by the front of the receiver. At this time the slide has compressed a coil spring seated in a hole drilled throughout its own length. The compressed spring drives the slide forward, carrying the bolt with it. The bolt picks up the topmost cartridge from the magazine and loads it into the chamber. The slide continues forward and the cam recess which first unlocked the bolt now turns it back into its locked position. The slide comes to rest against the gas piston and the carbine is ready to fire another round. This entire cycle occurs in about one eight hundredth of a second, so that the time required for reaiming is the only delay between the successive delivery of aimed shots.

The carbine has undergone several minor changes since its inception. The original push-through safety was replaced by a small lever, because men tended to mistake the magazine release for the safety, dropping the magazine out of the weapon. The sights were also changed, as previously described.

There have been two major alterations which changed the model designation. The first of these was known as the M1A1 carbine, which was identical with the M1 except for the stock. The M1A1 was intended chiefly for use by parachute troops and to fit within their requirements was equipped with a folding steel skeleton stock. The forward part of the stock was the same as that for the M1; behind the receiver tang, however, it was cut off, and a wooden pistol grip was attached to the rear of the stock. The folding stock was hinged to the rear of the wooden stock; when not in use it could be folded around the left side of the weapon.

The second model of the basic carbine, known as the M2, is designed to fire either semiautomatically or at full automatic, the weapon spewing out bullets as long as the trigger is held back. A selector switch, mounted on the left side of the receiver will, when engaged, act as sear trip, allowing the hammer to swing forward immediately after the bolt is locked, and as long as the trigger is held, allow the loading, firing, and ejection cycle to continue uninterruptedly. Contrary to popular belief, merely filing down the sear of an M1 rifle or carbine will not make it full automatic. The failure of such a conversion stems from two causes. First of all, the bolt must be fully locked before a chambered cartridge can be fired. The firing pin has a tang which must be aligned in a slot in the receiver bridge before it can be driven forward. If one manages to disconnect the sear, the hammer, not being held back in its cocked position, will follow the bolt as it moves forward, striking the firing pin a weak mushy blow. A weapon so altered will usually fire one or two rounds and then quit. The selector lever of the M2 carbine acts as a definite delay, permitting the hammer to snap forward only after the bolt is locked and thus imparts a sharp blow to the firing pin. The M2, which has a selector switch on the left of the receiver and a bayonet stud mounted on a sleeve on the barrel, is in other respects identical to the M1. A thirty-round box magazine, interchangeable with the fifteen-round magazine, has been made for the carbine. When fired fully automatic, the M2 carbine has a tremendously rapid cyclic rate of fire, from seven hundred and fifty to seven hundred and seventy-five rounds a minute.

The ammunition for the caliber .30 carbine consists of a rimless cartridge case which, while apparently cylindrical, is actually slightly tapered from the base to a short distance from the mouth; thereafter it is cylindrical. The entire round is 1.68 inches long, loaded with fourteen and a half grains of smokeless powder behind a one hundred and eleven grain-round nosed bullet. The powder is the propellant known as ball powder, and is currently receiving much attention as the charge for our new test rifles. In brief, it consists of small dense spheres of nitrocellulose, made under water, which are coated with nitroglycerine and an outer coating of a deterrent to reduce the initial burning rate. The grains are then glazed with graphite and mixed in proportions necessary to produce the desired chamber pressure and velocity. In the carbine cartridge, it develops a chamber pressure of about forty thousand pounds per square inch, driving the bullet out of the muzzle at 1,970 feet per second. The bullet is composed of a lead alloy core covered by gilding metal or steel coated with gilding metal. It is short and round-nosed, quite similar in shape to that of the caliber .45 automatic pistol bullet, and its velocity drops rapidly after it leaves the muzzle. However, it will penetrate twelve seven-eights-inch pine boards at 100 yards, eight boards at 200 yards, and seven boards at 300 yards. A tracer round, whose bullet tip may be painted either red or orange, is also an item of issue. The bullet, consisting of a lead alloy slug, a tracer and igniter compound, and a steel jacket clad with gilding metal, weighs slightly less than the ball ammunition bullet, one hundred and seven grains.

Where Do We Go from Here?

THUS far, we have seen the military shoulder arm develop from the clumsy flintlock musket to the semiautomatic rifle. Accuracy and rapidity of fire have improved, from slow and almost total inability to connect with the target, to a literal hose-stream of fire which can reach out a mile or so.

Almost anyone with normal eyesight and physical makeup can take an M1 rifle, after a short course of instruction, and place most of his shots into a twenty-inch circle from a distance of 500 yards. The bullets streak across almost a half mile of moving air and land extremely close to where the sights are pointed; and this, not from a special target rifle, but from a mass-produced item turned out by the millions. It is deadly, beyond the most eccentric dreams of the colonial marksman.

And yet the rifle is, for the main infantry weapon, in a peculiar position. A glance at an Army TO&E shows that there are more carbines, for instance, than there are rifles in any infantry division. This is, of course, due to the enormous number of men who operate crew-served weapons, or handle staff, supply, and communications work. But the fact is that the main reliance for fire power has been taken out of the rifleman's hands. Artillery and mortar fire, tank and machine gun, do the majority of the shooting.

Why then, have riflemen at all? This is certainly not a new idea. Each new weapon has its advocates, most of whom have a built-in missionary urge, who claim that the infantryman is rendered useless by whatever new device they are touting. The tank, though it shocked the world by lumbering across the width of France in forty days, did not diminish the use of infantry during the times of its greatest employment. And of course the plane was the key to quick victory. Only a few years ago, we actually believed those who claimed that airpower and precision bombing would reduce the Axis nations to quick surrender. May I remind them that foreign territory was won and held by men who walked, not flew, from the Normandy seacoast to Czechoslovakia. The biggest machine war in the earth's history was also the biggest

[188]

infantry war. It may seem as though an obvious point is being overemphasized, but too often we tend to lose sight of it. This is not intended as a criticism of any machine or any branch of service. What we must remember is that any new destructive invention, and its countermeasures, place both contending nations on the same relative footing they had before that given invention came into use.

The point is that only infantrymen can take and *hold* new territory; they are the only people who can compete with other foot soldiers on equal terms. An Army can level its cataclysmic strength at a single hillside and plaster it with enough artillery and mortar fire to make the scenery resemble something out of Macbeth. Planes zoom over, gutting the landscape with HE and jellied gasoline. Tanks claw and clank over the terrain, and rake the ground with cannon and machine gun fire. No one, you think, could survive that—thunderclap. Yet when the smoke clears and the dust settles, the rifleman is still in his hole; he's taken casualties, and he's punchy from noise and concussion and the fear of death; but he's still there, he's still dangerous, and he must be pried loose by other infantrymen. The machine has expended its utmost, and failed to dislodge him. And anyone who thinks differently will wake up on a stretcher with an inverted bottle of plasma suspended over his head.

Granted that wars in the foreseeable future will still employ riflemen, the cardinal problem is not how to reduce infantry strength, but how to improve its effectiveness. Quick mobility is not necessarily the same thing as quick killing, no matter who says so. Most of the late mechanized developments, such as the plane and the tank, are actually means of transporting weapons to the target in a hurry. Of itself, the plane cannot fight, but it can transport weapons at tremendous speeds and get away just as fast. The tank is a vehicle whose maneuverability and capacity to sustain weight enable it to carry heavy weapons and armor to protect them as human muscle could never do. But fundamentally, they are carriers, not weapons in themselves. No one seems to be against providing the utmost fire power to machines designed to move in and out of combat rapidly, but the same principle applied to the rifleman always causes considerable argument. The rifleman doesn't need a quick means of getting to the scene of combat; he's already there, he needs the other half of the mobility fire power combination; and advancements in design should be made with the idea of increasing the fire power of the one man who lives in the target area.

Almost everyone with more than one stripe on his sleeve has ventured an opinion on the desirability of a military rifle capable of full automatic fire. Those who are against it usually base their argument on the fact that casualties are produced only by those bullets which actually strike the target, and that volume of fire by itself is of no value. Quite true. But we seem to have heard the same words and tune sung before; prior to the Civil War, in fact. Unfortunately for the argument, combat goes on in darkness as well as daylight, on all terrain under all conditions, and against an enemy who is doing his utter damndest to avoid stopping a bullet himself. The well-defined stationary target, an easily discernible machine gun nest, for instance, is a much rarer sight on the battlefield than one would think. But the beefed-up rifle squad, which has scrounged up an extra BAR or a light machine gun is a very common sight. The men took these weapons, not because they liked carrying around the extra weight, but because they liked automatic fire around *when* they needed it. Which is what the light automatic rifle does—it may fire as slowly and as accurately as one wishes, or it may provide full auto fire in those brief desperately important moments when a great volume of fire is needed—night attacks, street fighting, breaking up charges by a numerically superior enemy, night perimeter defense, and so on.

Admittedly, singly delivered aimed shots are the key to precision shooting. Every war has its recorded instances of remarkable shots, in which enemy personnel were killed at fantastic ranges, perhaps as great as 1,000 yards. But these are abnormal shots, not normal ones. Though they highlight the story, they do not form the main continuous thread of it. We are dealing with warfare, not target shooting, and most of the fire comes from men of variable quality, trained, of necessity, under limited conditions of time. Getting down to the practical side of it, we find that most of the men in a rifle company have, at one time or another, gotten creditable scores at 200, 300, and 500 yards on a known distance target range. As a result, they could probably hit a standing man at 500 yards. These same men, after seeing what their rifles could do under optimum circumstances, were then put through their paces under less ideal ones. The next step in training was taken on the transition range, where they fired at popup targets which appeared at unknown ranges. Firing was done under limited time and from positions which a man would be likely to assume in combat; the men fired from behind logs, from dug-in positions, through windows, and so on. The whole transition stage was still in keeping with the doctrine of accurate-aimed fire, but with a view towards increasing the complexity of the circumstances under which it was done, by requiring the men to estimate their own ranges, learn to hold their sights over or under the target, assume hasty positions, and fire at targets which were visible only for seconds. The next

[190]

step, field firing, presented them with the great apparent paradox of military rifle firing—all this accurate aimed fire had to be directed against ill-defined and even invisible targets! This was done by the squad leader's pointing out the target *area* as best he could and assigning a sector of fire to each squad member, who fired into his sector at points where he thought the enemy would most likely be. Its effectiveness depended upon team work, fire discipline, and personal control of the most intense sort by the squad leader, if the system were to work at all. It is a rare rifle squad which can bring out the full capabilities of aimed yet guessed fire under these conditions.

To offset this difficulty, we find that most area fire is done by weapons capable of doing a far better job of it than the rifle—artillery, mortars, and machine guns. That which has been the rifleman's prime function over the centuries has been taken away from him. High explosive concentrations form the great mass of fire, and men soon learn to depend on it. The net result has been to make the rifle an even more personal weapon, one which must perform all its functions of attack and defense when the expected help from supporting fire fails to come or is nullified by weather, terrain, or conditions of visibility. The full auto rifle does not constitute any offense against the doctrine of aimed fire; it can do that as well as its forebears. And it can do more. When artillery fails to root out its target, when enemy troops break through barrages and final protective lines of fire, the soldier will be armed with a weapon eminently suited to protecting himself when the normal means of firepower have failed or been exhausted. For that's what the full auto rifle is—something extra, something else to bank on.

The definite need for full automatic rifles became apparent in the opening stages of the Pacific campaign. Word came back that armorers in that theater were successfully altering M1 carbines to fire automatically, and the design was used stateside, to come out as the M2 carbine. It was a natural step to apply the same line of reasoning to the M1 rifle. The prototypes of the semi-full automatic rifle were made in the latter portion of the war, when an order was placed for M1 rifles with selectors, much like those on the M2 carbines, to enable them to fire either full or semiautomatically. The sudden end of the war resulted in the cancellation of the order and the next time an automatic rifle cropped up was in the form of an experimental rifle known as the T-20, another standard M1 rifle with a full auto selector switch, a muzzle brake, and what appeared to be a BAR magazine protruding from the bottom of the stock. There was also an experimental job known as the T-25, which never received much publicity. It looked vaguely like the new British rifle; its stock was in straight prolongation of the barrel, giving it the

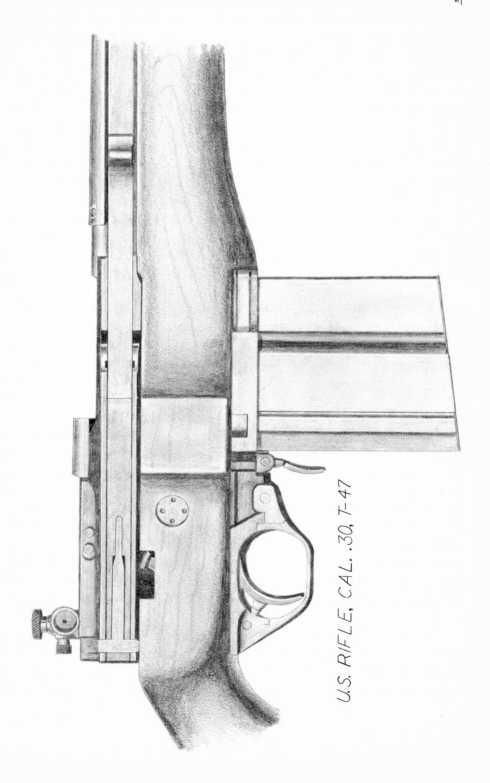

SHIELDS

U.S. RIFLE, CAL. .30, T-47

crutch-like silhouette of various foreign machine guns and automatic rifles. The Army has never taken kindly to the straight stock idea, basing its dislike on the fact that the stock forces a man to raise his head higher than necessary when firing a weapon so equipped. The T-25 also possessed some miserable hinged sights, set far above the top of the rifle, which were easily damaged. However the T-25 had a detachable twenty-round box magazine and a muzzle brake, and pointed the way towards future rifles. Then more silence. For some reason, most of the developmental program was kept secret, though there is nothing really startling about a semiautomatic rifle with a selector switch. However, the British stole some of the Army's thunder by unveiling *their* new rifle as a candidate for NATO's proposed standardized shoulder weapon, and the United States was forced to release its new rifle as a counter-irritant. In January, 1952, two new rifles, the T-47 and the T-44, were shown to the public for the first time, along with some data on their new cartridges, which seem to have caused more stir than the rifles themselves.

The T-47 operates on the same principle as the old Browning Automatic Rifle. As in both the BAR and M1, gas is tapped through a port in the underside of the barrel, and impinges against the piston head of an operating rod which extends back to the bolt. When the rifle is fired, the bolt is carried rearward by the operating rod, and in so doing, pulls a locking bolt downward out of a recess in the receiver. Continued rearward movement, once the action has been unlocked, extracts and ejects the empty case, compresses a spring for return movement, and cocks the action. As the bolt clears the space over the top of the magazine, a new round is fed into the return path of the bolt, and the forward motion of the bolt picks up a new round out of the magazine and locks it into the chamber. The rifle is 43 inches long, the same as the M1, but is about one and one half pounds lighter. The sights are of conventional type, a blade front sight protected by metal wings, and a receiver rear sight, adjustable in clicks for both windage and elevation. The stock is made from laminated strips of wood, a principle employed by the Germans throughout most of World War II. Laminated stocks are easily made, and do not warp or swell in bad weather. Recoil has been reduced by a muzzle brake, a slotted steel cylinder mounted on the muzzle.

The T-44, the other experimental rifle, looks like what it is, an M1 rifle action modified by a selector switch, enabling it to fire either automatically or semiautomatically. Like the T-47, it is fed through a twenty-round box magazine, and its other dimensions and features correspond roughly with

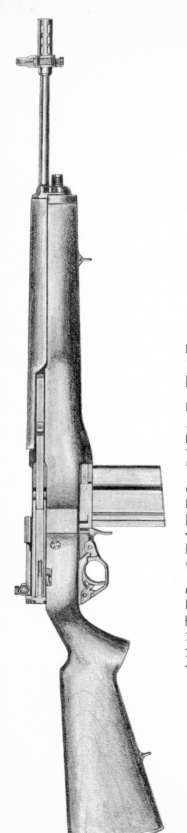

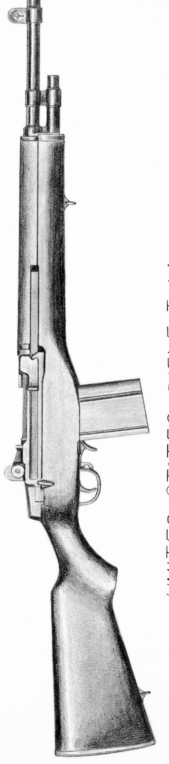

UNITED STATES RIFLE, T-47

UNITED STATES RIFLE, T-44

SHIELDS

those of the T-47. Along with its brother, the T-44 employs a recoil-reducing muzzle brake.

Since the muzzle brake is, except for main tank armament and some obsolete aircraft machine guns, something entirely new in United States military weapons, let us take a closer look at it and see what it is and what it does. For we didn't use them before; there must be a reason for their employment. Brother Newton expressed it all some years back, "For every action, there is always an equal and opposite reaction." When a rifle is fired, the gas expanding inside the cartridge and the barrel pushes with equal force in all directions. Being contained on all sides by the barrel, it is free to employ a noticeable effect in only two directions—forward and backward. The forward vector serves to drive the bullet out of the barrel. The rearward component shoves the rifle to the rear. The bullet is driven forward as the rifle is driven rearward and moves farther and faster chiefly because it is lighter than the rifle from which it was fired; in either case, the total energy expended is much the same. Once the burning gases clear the muzzle, they form a pocket of highly active material thrown suddenly into a space heretofore occupied by pure air, and their thrust, smashing against the rifle muzzle, accelerates it to the rear. The sum total of it all is the punishing few of which are impractical. The most obvious way is to reduce the power of the cartridge, an unacceptable method, because the rifle cartridge has a given job to do. The second is to increase the weight of the rifle, which by increasing its inertia, would reduce recoil. Equally unacceptable, for obvious reasons. Changes in stock design can be of some help. The wider the butt plate of a rifle, the more surface area it exposes to the shooter's shoulder, with a corresponding reduction in recoil per unit area. By the same token, a blunt knife cuts with more difficulty than a razor's edge. However, most military rifle butt plates are comfortably large, and one cannot improve on that to any extent. There is one trick, much used in commercial sporters, which the military might adopt. This is the employment of a stock with what is known as a Monte Carlo comb, one which slopes down from the butt plate towards the muzzle end. In recoil, this stock slides past the shooter's cheek, rather than bashing against it, as do most military rifle stocks.

But the largest controlable factor in recoil is that jet of gases escaping at the muzzle. All major improvements to date have been aimed at reducing that thrust which takes place at the muzzle and amounts to as much as a quarter of the rifle's kick. In principle, all such recoil-reducing devices, kick of a high power rifle. It can be reduced in a number of ways, all but a known as muzzle brakes, are the same. They trap some of the gas at the muzzle and deflect it to the side or rear, producing an actual forward push at the muzzle, opposite in direction to the recoil thrust. By varying the pitch of the holes or slots in the brake, one can reduce muzzle climb by allowing gas to escape through the top and thus push the muzzle down, or nullify any tendency of the muzzle to move sideways. What's the disadvantage? Blast. The gas which formerly moved away from the shooter is now deflected towards him, and to some people, at any rate, is more objectionable than recoil. Ironically, the more efficient the brake, the more racket it makes, and the reduction in recoil is directly proportional to its general unpleasantness.

These gadgets, decidedly unpleasant to use, were never employed heretofore in domestic military rifles, partly because of that disagreeable rumpus and blast and partly because the rifle barrel always had time to settle down between shots. The mass, the bulk of a rifle lies below the line of the barrel, and free recoil is prevented by the shooter's shoulder. When fired, the force pushing rearward must be expended some way, and the rifle rotates upward at the muzzle, using the firer's shoulder as a pivot. In slow fire, the rifle drops back into position between shots, but in full auto fire, the repeated succession of upward movements swings the muzzle skyward, not to mention the awful jolt of rapidly delivered fire. The muzzle brake, which cuts both muzzle climb and recoil, must be used to prevent all but the first shot of a burst from going wild of the target.

In July, 1950, the writer was taking ten on one of the ranges at Ft. Benning, Georgia, in an area which had been used both for firing and as an impact area. Rain erosion had washed away some topsoil, and there were literally thousands of empty cartridge cases and spent bullets exposed to view. After scrounging around I decided that there was nothing worth picking up in all that litter of cases; that is, none save two. They were both empty brass cases, bottlenecked rimless jobs, neither of which I could identify. The longer of the two, stamped FA 48 on the base, seemed obviously a cutdown case converted from GI fodder by a local gun crank. The other, stamped RG 49 280/30, was completely unfamiliar. Both of them went into my pocket, from there to my footlocker, and at length found their way into my desk drawer, where they are today. Over a year went by before the unveiled data of a new British Army rifle and cartridge sent me scuttling through a deskful of loose objects to discover that for months I had been sitting on top of the two latest cartridge developments, albeit empty cases. That stamped lettering, it turned out, stood for Radford Green 1949, caliber .280, powder charge, thirty grains. It was a fired case from the

British experimental rifle, the EM-2, which the British want adopted as the rifle for NATO. The British have a much greater need for a better military rifle than does the United States, and were apparently willing to accept lower standards. As has been pointed out repeatedly in many recent publications, the British round is considerably less peppy than the United States service cartridge. Its high trajectory lessens the length of grazing fire attainable when the cartridge is used in a machine gun; its lessened diameter increases the difficulty of equipping it with specialized bullets, such as tracers; and its lessened power reduces the chances of the rifle's operating effectively under Arctic conditions.

What is of interest to us, however, is that Frankford Arsenal cartridge case, identified the following January as the T-65, the round for which future Government weapons will be chambered. It looks like a squeezed-down .30-06 cartridge, and that's exactly what it is. In recent years, the manufacture of improved smokeless powder left the cartridge case with about a half inch of air space between the top of the powder charge and the bottom of the bullet, as the actual quantity of powder needed to achieve specified velocity was reduced. That half inch, formerly filled with powder, was now just wasted length and metal. The T-65 cartridge is that case without the wasted air space. The ballistics are the same for both rounds, the new cartridge performing the same job while remaining both lighter and smaller.

The new propellant is World War II ball powder, used in caliber .30 carbine cartridges, and used by the Orientals for some years. The explosive material is the same as for older ammunition, nitrocellulose, which is dissolved in water to form a sludge. Ethyl acetate, a volatile solvent, is added to the wet mixture, producing a solution quite similiar to model airplane dope or fingernail polish, celluloid dissolved in acetone. The liquid is pumped into tanks where mechanical agitation causes the small suspended particles of cellulose to adhere as small spheres. The solvent is evaporated from the solid material, and the dense spherical grains, pure nitrocellulose, are graded for size, because burning rate, remember, is dependent upon the size of the grains. The grains are then coated with nitroglycerine and a deterrent. The nitroglycerine furnishes the grain with more power and the deterrent reduces the initial rate of combustion, the combination of which forms a neutral rifle powder. Proper pressure and velocity are produced by mixing large and small grains in whatever proportions are needed.

It is no coincidence that new commercial sporting rifles are now on the market, chambered for a cartridge called the .308 Winchester, loaded with ball powder in a bottlenecked rimless case 51 mm long, about one-half-inch shorter than the .30-06. It duplicates the ballistics of the longer '06 ammunition, and for all practical purposes, is the same as the much touted and once highly secret T-65 cartridge.

It is a strange commentary on our way of running things that such ammunition will be used for shooting deer in this country instead of being sent to our troops overseas. Not a serious difficulty, of itself, because the new cartridge simply duplicates the performance of the old; it does not surpass it. The only saving lies in the realm of weight and space saving; and if the Army can stand it, so can I.

Before shouting unrestrained hosannas to the T-47, one should become aware of its limitations, for it has them, as does every other weapon. The important thing to remember about automatic fire is that one can't keep it up forever. A large percentage of the energy liberated by burning rifle powder, about 30%, is consumed in heating the barrel. It happens every time a round is fired, and the T-47 and T-44 rifles, which fire at a cyclic rate of over seven hundred rounds per minute, are quite capable of jamming and destroying themselves by sustained fire. Automatic fire is a specialized method of shooting, in automatic weapons with non-interchangeable barrels, and must be used with restraint. Ammunition expenditure and resupply, a very real and live problem, is of course sharply accented by the appearance of the automatic rifle.

Perhaps the whole idea of using gunpowder as a propellant is obsolete. It may be that some volatile liquid explosive, bottled in small replaceable cylinders like commercial CO_2, and ignited electrically, will furnish the power for weapons of the future. Undoubtedly, due to the scientific miracles which have recently come into being, long range experiments of the most incredible sort are under way. But whatever the Army knows, the Army isn't saying, and any guesswork would be just that. The only conclusion one can reach is to grope around rather lamely and repeat the statement made by Lt. Bennett some sixty-six years ago . . . "Some other explosive than gunpowder may solve the problem."

Glossary of Firearms Terms

A

AMMUNITION. The combination of propellant, primer, bullet, and cartridge case which comprise a complete cartridge.

ANVIL. The solid surface against which an explosive primer mixture is smashed in order to initiate combustion.

ARMOR-PIERCING. *See* Bullet.

ARMORY. A building wherein weapons are manufactured and/or stored.

ARSENAL. A plant for the manufacture of ammunition. Originally two separate terms, arsenal and armory are used interchangeably.

AUTOLOADING. The functioning process by which a weapon will, when loaded and fired once, extract and eject the empty cartridge case, feed a fresh round into the chamber, and cock the weapon for another shot. There is a mechanical interruption at this point, and the trigger must be released and squeezed after each shot. These functions are performed by the power of the exploding propellant. *Semiautomatic. Selbstlader. Self-loader.*

AUTOMATIC. A weapon which when loaded and fired once, will extract and eject the empty case, reload a live round into the chamber, and cock and fire itself again in an uninterrupted cycle, so long as the trigger is held back or ammunition remains in the magazine. Such weapons are the true machine guns, submachine guns, and machine pistols, and should not be confused with the semiautomatic weapons, among them the so-called automatic pistols and shotguns, which are wrongly lumped into this class.

B

BALL. Originally a cast sphere of pure lead used as a small arms projectile. The subsequent and widespread use of rifling led to the adoption of cylindrical and conoidal bullets which would offer a wider bearing surface for the rifling. While obviously not spherical, these bullets were still known as balls. The term has lasted to this day, in that Government general-purpose ammunition is still referred to as ball ammunition.

BALL AMMUNITION. Today a generic term which includes small arms ammunition designed for anti-personnel use. It may contain bullets of lead hardened with tin or antimony, or lead jacketed with gilding metal.

[199]

BALL POWDER. A modern propellant composed of small dense spheres of nitro-cellulose coated with a layer of nitroglycerine and a deterrent. Ball powder, the propellant for the Army's new experimental rifles, was widely used during World War II as the load for carbine ammunition.

BALLISTICS. The study which treats the various forces and motions of moving projectiles. It is divided into two broad phases; interior ballistics, which covers bullets from the instant they are fired until they leave the muzzle, and exterior ballistics, which deals with bullets in free flight.

BALLISTIC COEFFICIENT. A number given to each type of bullet which indicates the extent to which it will be affected by air resistance. The larger the number, the closer the trajectory will approach the ideal curve produced by firing a missile in a vacuum.

BAND. A ring of metal, either stamped or machined, which encircles both the stock and barrel of a military shoulder arm. It is named after its position relative to the muzzle, the upper band being at the front end of the stock, close to the muzzle. The middle and/or lower bands are further back along the stock.

BAR. The common abbreviation for Browning Automatic Rifle, a heavy gas-operated automatic shoulder weapon issued out to infantry squads as their main source of fire power.

BARREL. The iron or steel tube of a gun which directs the projectile on its desired course.

BATTERY. *See* Frizzen.

BAYONET. A blade weapon capable of being affixed to the muzzle of a shoulder arm. Most of the early United States bayonets had a triangular fluted blade and a hollow cylindrical handle which slid over the first several inches of the barrel.

The Spanish-American War brought about the general use of knife bayonets, dagger-type weapons which were locked to the rifle by a ring cut into the bayonet guard and a spring catch and groove in the haft of the bayonet.

BELL CRANK. In lever action rifles, an eccentric lever attached slidably to the carrier block at one end and pivoted to the trigger guard lever at the other. Depressing the lever causes the bell crank to lift the carrier block, with its fresh cartridge, in line with the chamber of the barrel for feeding.

BERDAN PRIMER. *See* Primer.

BLACK POWDER. A mechanical mixture of finely divided charcoal, sulphur, and potassium nitrate. It is usually made in the form of small black grains glazed with graphite. Black powder is graded by size according to whichever size sieve the grains will pass through. In order of decreasing size, the grains are known as FG, FFG, and FFFG, and in a general way, the smaller the grain, the faster the burning rate.

BLUING. An oxidizing process which is used to color metal in various shades of blue and tends to prevent rust. Usually accomplished by boiling the metal parts in a bath of metallic salts and water.

BOLT. A cylindrical or rectangular steel assembly which seals the breech of a rifle during firing and supports the base of the cartridge case. Normally, a rifle bolt is hollowed out to enclose a spiral mainspring and a firing pin and striker, and is shaped on the outside to form a bolt handle and one or more locking lugs.

BOLT FACE. The forward end of the bolt, centrally drilled to permit the protrusion of the striker.

BOLT HANDLE. The bar of steel which protrudes past the stock at right angles to the long axis of the bolt, and usually terminates in a spherical knob. Turning the handle through an arc of ninety degrees frees the locking lugs from their recesses and allows the bolt to be withdrawn straight to the rear.

BOLT HEAD. The forward section of a two-piece bolt.

BOLT SLEEVE. The steel machining at the rear of the bolt which serves to unite all the components of the bolt assembly.

BORE. The axially bored hole in a gun barrel through which the bullet is driven by expanding powder gases.

BOXER PRIMER. *See* Primer.

BREECH. The rear end of a gun barrel. Often used to include all the mechanism to the rear of the barrel.

BREECH BLOCK. Any steel device used to seal the breech of a rifle at the instant of firing. The bolt is a form of breech block.

BREECH-LOADER. Any firearm which is loaded through the rear or breech end, as opposed to loading through the forward or muzzle end.

BROWN BESS. A military slang name given to the flintlock muskets with which eighteenth-century British troops were armed.

BULLET. A missile fired from a gun.

1. ARMOR PIERCING. A bullet built of a hard-steel core supported fore and aft by soft lead, the whole being enclosed in a gilding metal jacket. Upon impact, the core strips through its enfolding jacket and continues through the target.

2. BALL. Today an anti-personnel round composed of a lead alloy core jacketed with gilding metal.

3. FRANGIBLE. A training bullet designed to be fired directly against target planes. Its construction, 50% bakelite and 50% powdered lead, allows it to disintegrate upon impact.

4. INCENDIARY. A bullet filled with a compound which produces intense heat upon impact.

5. METAL JACKETED. Loosely, any bullet whose core is covered with a fairly hard envelope of metal.

6. METAL PATCHED. Originally, a bullet whose jacket covered all but the lead nose. Today, jackets cover the entire bullet, which has led to the use of the term *full metal patched.*

7. TRACER. A bullet whose open base contains an incendiary compound which is ignited by firing the gun. Its flight is visible for a distance of about one thousand yards.

BUTT PLATE. A metal plate screwed to the rear of a musket or riflestock, designed to protect it from splitting and chipping.

BUTTSTOCK. The rear portion of a musket or riflestock.

[201]

CALIBER. The inside diameter of a gun barrel. In this country, caliber is usually measured in hundredths of an inch (.30, .45, etc.). In England the practice is to designate the diameter in thousandths, such as .303 or .455. In Europe and Asia caliber is measured in millimeters, as 7.62 or 9 mm. The designated caliber may have little to do with the actual diameter, due to trade names and the fact that diameter can be measured three separate ways, across both lands, across both grooves, or across one land and one groove.

In heavy weapons such as artillery pieces, caliber is used to express the relationship between the inside barrel diameter and the length of the barrel. A 5-inch .38 artillery piece would fire a projectile 5 inches in diameter through a barrel 190 inches or 15 feet, 10 inches in length.

CANNELURE. An annular groove cut into the base of a cartridge case. A groove cut around the circumference of a bullet, which may be filled with lubricant or used as a seat for crimping the bullet into the cartridge case.

CARBINE. A short musket or rifle, usually issued to mounted troops or more recently, troop commanders or operators of crew-served weapons. While ordinarily a shortened version of any given infantry rifle, the carbine may be an entirely different weapon, a case illustrated by the M1 rifle and M1 carbine.

CARRIER BLOCK. In lever action rifles, a metal elevator which is attached to the lever by a bell crank. Pressure from the magazine spring forces a live round into a recess in the block. A downward movement of the lever lifts the carrier block into position at the breech end of the barrel, so that the cartridge can be fed into the chamber.

CARTRIDGE. Today, a self-contained unit comprising bullet, cartridge case, propellant, and primer. Prior to the invention of the metallic cartridge, the term applied to any attempt to combine several of the above elements into one housing, such as a paper sack containing a bullet and a measured amount of powder.

1. CENTER-FIRE. A cartridge whose primer is seated in a depression in the center of the base of the cartridge. Combustion can be started only by a blow in the center of the case.

2. RIMFIRE. A cartridge whose soft rim is filled with priming compound, so that it can be ignited by a blow at any point around its circumference. Once the standard method of ignition, the rimfire has survived today only in the .22 cartridge.

CARTRIDGE CASE. A rigid weatherproof brass housing into which the various components of a complete cartridge are loaded. Cartridge cases may be classed, according to shape, into straight case and tapered case, which are just what their names imply; and the modern bottleneck case. This latter case has a large powder capacity and a small bullet, so the case narrows abruptly at a point called the shoulder into a small cylindrical neck, into which the bullet is crimped.

1. RIMMED. A cartridge case whose base is larger than the rest of the case.

The rim serves as a grip for the extractor and prevents the case from going too far into the chamber.

2. RIMLESS. A cartridge whose base is no larger than some point forward of the base. Such cases have an extracting cannelure cut around the base and are seated to proper depth in the chamber by the shoulder, the juncture of body and neck.

CASE HARDENING. A process whereby a metal surface is superficially hardened in order to resist wear. The metal is heated with some substance having a high carbon content, such as charred leather, bone, or charcoal, and quenched in oil. The steel then has a high percentage of carbon at the surface, and diminishes in carbon content towards the center. Depending on the use to which the metal will be put, it may be reheated and quenched again, tempered, and allowed to cool slowly.

CHAMBER. A hole drilled and reamed into the breech end of a gun barrel, and cut to the same shape as the cartridge which it houses.

CHARGER. *See* Clip.

CLIP. A brass or steel assembly designed to hold a given number of cartridges for loading into a rifle. The most familiar American variety is an eight-shot clip used in the M1 rifle. Cartridges and clip together are loaded into the magazine well of the rifle, a style known as *en bloc* loading.

Earlier varieties, such as those used in the M1903 Springfield, M1917 Enfield, and most other Mauser rifles, were of the true charger design. These clips were inserted into a set of slots cut into the receiver of the rifle and the cartridges were stripped off of them and into the magazine. The clip was then pulled out of the slots and thrown away.

CLIP SLOTS. A pair of guide grooves milled into the forward end of a rifle receiver bridge so as to hold a clip in position for loading.

COCK. In verb form, to ready a weapon for firing by compressing the mainspring, providing power for the hammer or striker to drive forward. On arms of flintlock vintage and earlier, the hammer itself was called a cock.

COCKING PIECE. In bolt action rifles, a steel rod, either cylindrical or mushroom-shaped and usually knurled, which protrudes past the rear of the bolt sleeve, forming the terminus of the rod about which the mainspring is coiled.

COMB. The ridge which forms the upper edge of a buttstock.

CORDITE. An early double base smokeless powder formed by absorbing nitroglycerine in guncotton, adding a small percentage of vaseline, and extruding the mixture through a die into long strings or cords.

CORE. The internal part of a bullet, that which is covered by the jacket.

CRIMP. To mechanically fold inward the mouth of a cartridge case about the base of the bullet, sealing it in place.

CUPRONICKEL. An alloy of about 60% copper and 40% nickel, formerly used in the manufacture of bullet jackets. During the 1920's it was superseded by *gilding metal*.

CUTOFF. A device used in magazine rifles to prevent the feeding of cartridges from the magazine while allowing the weapon to be loaded with single rounds, the idea being to keep the magazine loaded for emergencies. It has been used on many United States magazine rifles, notably the Spencer, M1878 Hotchkiss, M1882 Chaffee-Reece, M1882 Hotchkiss, Krag-Jörgensen, and M1903 Springfield.

CYCLIC RATE. The rate of fire in rounds per minute of an automatic weapon. In shoulder arms, it is invariably higher than the actual deliverable rate of fire, because of the time consumed in changing magazines.

D

DEGRESSIVE POWDER. A propellant whose surface area and rate of evolution of gas decreases as the powder burns. Any solid chunk of propellant, such as a sphere, cube, or cylinder, burns degressively.

DETERRENT. A compound or element which is added to an explosive to reduce its burning rate. It may be used as an outer coating or mixed with the explosive at some point during its manufacture.

DIPHENYLAMINE. A crystalline organic compound ($C_6 H_5$)$_2$ NH, formed by heating aniline with aniline hydrochloride. Used as a stabilizer in the manufacture of small arms propellants.

DOUBLE BASE POWDER. A propellant made by absorbing nitroglycerine in guncotton. This powder burns rapidly and is used mainly in short barreled weapons such as pistols and revolvers. It usually contains a small proportion of inorganic salts, such as potassium, to reduce flash and increase ease of ignition.

DRIFT. The horizontal movement of a bullet at right angles to its principal direction of flight. It is not the result of cross winds. When a bullet leaves the muzzle, it begins to drop, the same as any other unsupported object. The air below it is compressed slightly, and the spinning projectile rolls on this cushion of compressed air in the direction of its spin.

E

EJECTOR. A metal cam inside a rifle receiver against which a fired cartridge case is struck and thrown clear of the weapon.

ELEVATION. The distance a rear sight must be raised to compensate for bullet drop over any given range. Rear sights may have the distance scaled off on them or may be adjustable in clicks which move the strike of the bullet in fractions of degrees of angle.

ENERGY. The capacity to perform work, usually expressed in foot-pounds. The kinetic energy of a bullet is determined by dividing by two the product of its mass and the square of its velocity.

EXTRACTOR. A flexible metal claw which slips over the rim or extracting cannelure of a cartridge case as the gun breech is closed. As the breech is opened, the extractor pulls the fired case with it out of the chamber to a point where it strikes the ejector and is flipped out of the rifle.

[204]

F

FEEDING. The process of driving live cartridges from the magazine into the chamber of a firearm.

FEED RAMP. A slanted metal surface at the rear of a barrel which guides cartridges into the chamber during feeding.

FIRING PIN. A metal rod which transmits a hammer blow or thrust of the mainspring to the primer of the cartridge.

FLINT. A granular variety of quartz which fractures concoidally to a sharp edge. When struck against steel it produces a shower of sparks, and for this reason was used in early firearms to ignite the propellant.

FLINTLOCK. The ignition system for firearms by which the powder charge was ignited by a blow of flint upon steel. In military circles the flintlock was the chief weapon from about 1670 until 1842, when it was replaced by the percussion system.

FLOOR PLATE. The detachable metal cover at the bottom of the magazine well and in front of the trigger guard of a bolt action rifle. It forms a fixed surface against which the magazine spring is compressed by loading cartridges into the magazine.

FOLLOWER. The steel carrier which forms the upper terminus of a magazine spring.

FOLLOWER SPRING. A zigzag leaf spring which connects the follower and floor plate. Loading cartridges into the magazine compresses the spring, which maintains constant pressure upward towards the top of the magazine well. *Magazine Spring.*

FRIZZEN. The L-shaped piece of iron on the outside of a flintlock lock plate, pivoted at the juncture of the two arms of the L. The upper arm serves as the surface against which the flint strikes to shower sparks into the pan. The lower arm serves as the pan cover. Formerly called *battery.*

FRIZZEN SPRING. A U- or V-shaped spring on the outside of a flintlock lock plate which keeps the frizzen upright so that the pan is covered.

FRONT SIGHT. *See* Sights.

FULL PATCH. *See* Bullet.

FULMINATE OF MERCURY. A violent explosive $Hg(OCN)_2$, made by dissolving mercury in nitric acid and adding alcohol to it. For many years it was the only explosive effective as a primer or detonator. It has largely been replaced by Hexanitromannite, lead azide, and other non-corrosive compounds.

G

GAIN TWIST. A system of rifling in which the pitch of the lands and grooves increases from breech to muzzle in order to gradually accelerate a bullet to maximum rotational velocity as it leaves the muzzle.

GAS PORT. In gas-operated weapons, a small hole drilled into the barrel through which some of the expanding powder gases escape to furnish power for the auto-loading cycle.

GERMAN SILVER. A white alloy of copper, zinc, and nickel used experimentally as bullet jacket material.

GILDING METAL. An alloy of about 90% copper and 10% zinc used as a bullet jacket in modern ammunition. It has almost universally replaced cupronickel and other alloys as standard jacket material.

GRAPHITE. A soft form of pure carbon used as a lubricant and as a glaze for grains of propellant to prevent the buildup of static electricity and the attendant danger of premature explosions.

GROOVES. *See* Rifling.

GUNCOTTON. A high explosive formed by the action of sulphuric and nitric acids upon cellulose. Its shattering effect or brissance is too high for it to be used as a propellant, but when used with nitroglycerine and suitable amounts of solvents it forms the main ingredient of many modern rifle propellants.

H

HAMMER. An external metal part of a firearm which is held to the rear against spring tension, released by pulling the trigger, and is driven forward to fire the weapon.

In flintlock weapons, the hammer contained a pair of vise jaws which held a piece of flint. Percussion weapon hammers were characterized by a large spur for cocking and a concave striking face which enclosed a percussion cap.

In modern rifles, such as the M1, the hammer is completely enclosed within the rifle and when released strikes the rear of a firing pin.

HANDGUARD. A wood or metal cover which encloses the upper half of a rifle barrel and protects the firer's hands from heat generated by firing.

HEADSPACE. The distance between the face of a breech block and some fixed point against which a cartridge is seated when chambered. If this distance is excessive, due to wear or faulty machining or assembly, the brass cartridge case expands freely beyond its elastic limit and splits or ruptures, spilling hot gases into the action.

In rimmed cartridges, the forward end of the rim is seated against the rear end of the barrel, and headspace is the distance between the breech block and the breech end of the barrel.

In rimless bottleneck cartridges, the standard military cartridges in use today, the cartridge case is seated against the shoulder of the chamber where the neck of the case joins the body, preventing the case from going beyond a given distance. Thus the headspace is well over an inch, from the face of the breech block to the shoulder of the chamber.

HEEL. The upper rear corner of a rifle buttstock. The top of the butt plate.

HIGH EXPLOSIVES. Explosive compounds which are characterized by tremendous brissance or shattering power and convert their solids into gases at a rate entirely too fast for use as propellants.

I

IRON PYRITES. Sulphide of iron, which will produce sparks when struck against iron or steel. The wheel-lock firearms used pyrites for this purpose. Later weapons, the flintlocks, used flint as spark producers.

J

JACKET. A metal cover surrounding the soft metal (usually lead) core of a bullet.

JAWS. The two metal surfaces of a flintlock hammer, one fixed and one movable, which held a piece of flint in place.

K

KENTUCKY RIFLE. A flintlock or percussion muzzle-loading rifle, used by eighteenth- and nineteenth-century frontiersmen. It is characterized by a long heavy octagonal barrel, a bent-downward buttstock with a deep crescent butt plate, simple open sights, and rather small caliber. While known as the Kentucky rifle, the rifle's origin was in Lancaster County, Pennsylvania, and it is often called the Pennsylvania rifle.

KNURL. A series of ridges or beads on a metal surface to aid in grasping it without slipping.

L

LANDS. *See* Rifling.

LEVER ACTION. A rifle whose action is operated by a lever under the stock. The lever usually serves as a trigger guard as well as an actuating device.

LOAD. To insert cartridges or ammunition components into a gun to prepare it for firing.

LOADING GATE. In lever action rifles, a hinged cover on the right side of the receiver. Cartridges are loaded into the rifle by pressing them against the gate, which depresses and exposes the open end of the magazine.

LOCK. The entire firing mechanism of a muzzle-loading arm. In modern arms, the breech sealing assembly as well as the firing mechanism. To put the safety of a loaded gun in operative position to prevent accidental discharge.

LOCKING LUGS. Metal protuberances which form an integral part of a breech block and fit into a corresponding set of slots when the breech is closed, locking the gun for firing.

LOCK PLATE. A detachable flat metal plate to which all the lock mechanism of a side hammer weapon is affixed.

M

MAGAZINE. That part of a rifle which mechanically feeds single cartridges successively into a position where the forward movement of a breech block will pick up the uppermost cartridge and load it into the chamber. It may be an integral part of the rifle, as that on the M1903 Springfield, or a detachable unit, as in the M1882 Lee. Magazines may operate on any of a number of different feed systems, tubular, box, rotary, etc., but all of them employ a rigid housing containing a feed or follower spring and a follower.

MAINSPRING. A heavy spring in the mechanism of a gun which provides power for the forward movement of a hammer or striker.

MATCH. A long cord soaked in potassium salts which, when ignited, will burn and sputter for a long time.

MATCHLOCK. A primitive form of firearm in which a match was placed in the jaws of a serpentine or hammer. Pressing the trigger brought the hammer forward and rested the lighted match in the pan of the weapon, igniting the primer which in turn ignited the main charge.

MINIÉ BULLET. A cylindro-conoidal bullet with a hollow base which expanded into engagement with the rifling under the power of burning propellant gases. Named after E. C. Minié, a French Infantry Captain, the Minié Bullet was the universal small arms projectile of the American Civil War.

MUSKET. A smoothbore military shoulder arm.

MUZZLE. The open end of a gun barrel from which the bullet enters free flight.

MUZZLE BLAST. The disagreeable and violent disturbance at the muzzle of a gun, caused by expanding gas escaping into the atmosphere.

MUZZLE BRAKE. A slotted tube affixed to the muzzle of a rifle which traps part of the escaping gas and deflects it towards the direction of recoil, producing a counter-recoil thrust.

N

NECK. The forward part of a bottlenecked cartridge, reduced in diameter to the size of the bullet it contains.

NEUTRAL POWDER. A propellant whose surface area and rate of evolution of gas remains constant as the powder burns. This is attained by casting the propellant into monoperforated geometric forms, so that as the outside area burns and decreases, the inner surface burns and increases the area exposed to combustion. Neutral powders form the bulk of modern military shoulder arms propellants.

NIPPLE. In percussion weapons, a small metal tube screwed into the breech end of the barrel. When a percussion cap is placed on the open top of the nipple and struck by the hammer, the cap produces a flame which passes through the nipple into the barrel and fires the main charge of propellant.

NITROCELLULOSE. *See* Guncotton.

NITROGLYCERINE. Glyceryl nitrate, formed by the action of sulphuric and nitric acids upon glycerin, a trihydroxyl alcohol. This explosive, totally unstable, was made famous by Alfred Nobel, who harnessed it by absorbing it in inert infusorial earth. With the droplets of liquid thus dispersed, the mixture became the relatively stable explosive, dynamite. Today, nitroglycerine is used in the manufacture of double base powders.

O

OBTURATOR. A breech sealing device which prevents the escape of gas as a gun is fired. In small arms, this function is performed by the brass cartridge case.

P

PAN. The small cup-shaped metal forging on the lockplate of a flintlock arm, used to hold the priming powder.

PARKERIZING. A gray non-reflecting finish imparted to modern military rifles. It is achieved by sand-blasting the metal and boiling it in a solution of powdered iron and phosphoric acid.

PATCH. A small piece of fabric or leather which was wrapped around the bullet of a muzzle-loading rifle. The patch prevented the escape of gas past the bullet and also engaged the rifling, allowing the use of small, easily-loaded bullets without any loss of accuracy.

PATCH BOX. A cutaway section of a muzzle-loading rifle buttstock, fitted with a hinged cover and used to carry patches and other accouterments.

PENNSYLVANIA RIFLE. *See* Kentucky Rifle.

PERCUSSION CAP. A small copper cup filled with explosive and waterproofed at its open end by a piece of metal foil. It is placed over the nipple of a percussion shoulder arm and fires the main charge upon being struck by the hammer. The percussion cap was used on United States military arms from the 1840's until the close of the Civil War.

PERCUSSION LOCK. A gun lock designed for use with a percussion cap. Its salient features were a metal side hammer and a nipple affixed to the breech end of the barrel.

PISTOL GRIP. The lower edge of a buttstock just behind the trigger guard which has been shaped so as to resemble the stock of a pistol. It is used to give the trigger hand a more comfortable grip.

PITCH. The number of turns made by rifling per unit length. It is usually expressed in turns per inch. Often called the twist of the rifling.

POTASSIUM NITRATE. A strong oxidizing agent, KNO_3, one of a number of the salts of nitric acid. One of the first such compounds to be discovered, it has long been of military importance as the basic ingredient of black powder.

POWDER. In its broadest sense, any firearms propellant. The main types are black powder and smokeless powder, which is not powder at all, but a cast form of nitrated organic compounds.

PRIMER. A small charge of sensitive explosive used to detonate a larger and less sensitive amount of explosive. In modern metallic cartridges there are two types of primers in general use.

1. BERDAN PRIMER. A center-fire primer, popular in Europe and Asia, whose anvil is constructed out of part of the cartridge case.

2. BOXER PRIMER. The center-fire primer favored in the United States. It is a completely self-contained unit whose anvil is a small metal cone inside the primer cup.

PRIMER CUP. The cartridge copper housing which contains the components of a center-fire primer.

PRIMER POCKET. The cylindrical depression in the rear of a center-fire cartridge case which holds the primer cup.

PRIMER VENT. A small hole drilled through the primer pocket to allow flame from the exploding primer to reach and ignite the main charge.

PROGRESSIVE POWDER. A propellant whose surface area and rate of evolution of gas increases as the powder burns. Such propellants are made in the form of multiperforated grains which expose a progressively larger surface area to combustion as burning continues. Their use is usually confined to artillery pieces.

PROPELLANT. Any explosive which burns slowly enough to be used to drive a bullet out of a gun.

PYROCELLULOSE. Nitrated cellulose with a nitrogen content less than that of guncotton, 12.6% as against 13.4%.

R

RAMROD. A metal or wooden rod used to ram the wad and bullet down the barrel of a muzzle-loading weapon.

RECEIVER. The steel forging which forms the basic housing for all the operating components or lockwork of a rifle and to which the barrel and stock are attached.

RECEIVER BRIDGE. The arched rear portion of a rifle receiver.

RECEIVER RING. The front end of a rifle receiver, threaded for the insertion of the barrel.

RECOIL. The rearward thrust of a fired gun, caused by the reaction of gases which push the bullet out of the barrel. It is measured in foot pounds in a direction in prolongation of the line of the gun barrel. Since the shooter's shoulder is below this line, the muzzle tends to swing upward, using the shoulder as a pivot.

RIFLE. A shoulder arm whose barrel is engraved with spiral grooves.

RIFLE MUSKET. A term used during the Civil War to designate those shoulder arms which, while employing rifled barrels, retained the outside dimensions of the old smoothbore muskets.

RIFLING. A series of spiral grooves cut in the bore of a barrel which impart a spin to the bullet. The two features are known as lands and grooves, the lands being the raised or uncut portion of the rifling.

SAFETY. A mechanical device which blocks the firing parts of a weapon to prevent accidental discharge.

SALTPETER. *See* Potassium Nitrate.

SEAR. The mechanism operating between the trigger and the hammer or striker, its object being to provide a smooth letoff as the trigger is pulled.

SEAR NOSE. The upper extremity of the trigger or any series of levers acting in continuation of the trigger.

SEAR NOTCH. A depression cut into a hammer or a firing pin which is engaged by the sear nose when the weapon is cocked. Pressure on the trigger drops the sear nose out of engagement with the notch and allows the firing mechanism to drive forward.

SECTIONAL DENSITY. A mathematical symbol expressing the relationship between a bullet's weight and its diameter. It is found by dividing the total weight by the square of the diameter. The higher the sectional density, the less cross sectional area per unit weight is exposed to air resistance.

SEMIAUTOMATIC. *See* Autoloading.

SERPENTINE. The primitive S-shaped hammer of a matchlock arm.

SIGHTS. The aiming devices on firearms; mechanical or optical aids in pointing a gun at a target.

1. FRONT SIGHT. A metal blade, attached to the upper side of a barrel near the muzzle, which aids in keeping the barrel pointed towards the target.

2. REAR SIGHT. The sight closest to the breech of a rifle. It has passed through many development stages, the chief of which are listed below.

(a) OPEN SIGHT. A small vertical plate mounted on top of the barrel. It contains a V-notch, into which the front sight is centered vertically and transversely to aim the weapon at the target.

(b) LEAF SIGHT. A form of open sight which is hinged at its juncture with the barrel, so that it can be raised higher above the barrel as range increases, compensating for gravity's effect on the moving bullet. A common military form is shaped like a ladder with a single slidable rung which is pierced by an aperture or a notch. The slide may be held at any given point on the ladder, on which is engraved various ranges in hundreds of yards. Another form consists of a pair of inclined ramps cut in the shape of a parabola, the rough shape of the bullet's trajectory. Pushing the sight slide up the ramps serves to compensate for bullet drop.

(c) APERTURE SIGHT. A rear sight pierced by a circular hole through which the shooter aligns the front sight and the target. The normal practice today is to mount such sights well back towards the shooter's eye; such sights are called receiver sights, after their location on the rifle. However, both ramp and ladder sights may have apertures.

3. OPTICAL SIGHT. A sight which contains a series of lenses in a rigid housing. Although the sight need not magnify, a principle illustrated by the new British experimental rifle, most small arms optical sights are of the magni-

[211]

fying or telescopic variety, a completely self-contained system adjustable for both windage and elevation.

SINGLE BASE POWDER. A propellant whose explosive agent is made from pure nitrocellulose. It is the most common type of military powder in use today, chiefly because it burns less rapidly than the compound or double base variety.

SLING. A leather or fabric strap used for carrying a firearm.

SMALL. The narrow neck of wood between the comb of a riflestock and the point at which the stock joins the receiver or frame.

SMOKELESS POWDER. A variety of propellant which is not powder at all, but gelatinized nitrocellulose to which various compounds have been added in order to control burning rate and stability. It is usually manufactured in the form of small grains, flakes, pellets, or strips, which are either perforated or nonperforated. Depending upon the volume and rate of production of gas desired, smokeless powders are classed as degressive, neutral, or progressive.

SMOOTHBORE. A firearm whose barrel is not rifled. At one time the most common type of firearm, it has been universally replaced by rifled weapons, with the sole exception of shotguns.

SNAPHANCE. The earliest recorded form of flintlock. Believed to be of Dutch origin, the snaphance may be distinguished by a mainspring on the outer surface of the lock plate and a pan cover which had to be manually opened prior to firing.

STRIKER. The forward end of a firing pin.

SWIVEL. 1. SLING SWIVEL. An oval band of metal through which a sling is looped in order to attach it to a rifle or musket.

2. STACKING SWIVEL. An incomplete oval band, usually attached to the upper band of a military shoulder arm, used to lock weapons together in temporary triangular stacks.

T

TANG. A metal shank projecting rearward from a rifle receiver. It is bored with a hole into which the rear trigger guard screw is threaded in order to lock the gun action firmly into the stock.

TAPE PRIMER. A form of percussion cap in which small bits of explosive were sealed at regular intervals between two strips of paper. A roll of this tape was inserted in a specially designed rifle wherein each cocking motion of the hammer would place one pellet of the primer over the nipple of the weapon, where it was smashed by the falling hammer. Invented by Dr. Edward Maynard of Washington, the tape primer was much used just prior to the Civil War.

TERSULPHIDE OF ANTIMONY. An orange-colored compound formed when hydrogen sulphide is added to a solution of antimony ions. It is much used in the manufacture of explosive primers.

TRACER. *See* Bullet.

TRAJECTORY. The path, roughly parabolic, followed by a bullet in flight.

TRIGGER. A metal lever projecting from the bottom of a gun, which releases the firing mechanism upon being pulled.

TRIGGER GUARD. An oval loop of metal which surrounds the projecting part of a trigger. It is designed to prevent accidental firing.

TUMBLER. A part of the mechanism of side hammer lock shoulder arms. Essentially a flat piece of metal stock which rotates coaxially through the same arc as the hammer. Its lower surface is notched so it can be held by the sear when the hammer is pulled back into operative position.

TWIST. *See* Pitch.

V

VELOCITY. The speed with which a bullet travels, usually measured in feet per second.

W

WHEEL LOCK. The firearms ignition system used immediately prior to the invention of the snaphance. It consisted of a serrated wheel wound up against spring tension, touching a piece of iron pyrites. Pulling the trigger released the wheel which spun against the pyrites, showering sparks into a pan filled with priming powder, which in turn ignited the main charge.

WINDAGE. The lateral movement of a bullet in flight, caused by wind blowing across the bullet's trajectory.

Bibliography

PERIODICALS

American Rifleman. Washington, 1948–1952.
Army Information Digest. Washington, Government Printing Office, 1952–1953.
Gun Digest. The Gun Digest Company, Chicago, 1950–1953.

GOVERNMENT DOCUMENTS

Annual Report of the Chief of Ordnance to the Secretary of War for the Fiscal Year Ended June 30, 1879. Washington, Government Printing Office, 1879.
Annual Report of the Chief of Ordnance. 1880, 1881, 1882, 1883, 1884, 1885, 1886, 1887, 1888, 1889, 1890, 1891, 1895, 1899, 1900, 1902, 1903, 1904, 1905, 1906, 1907. Washington, Government Printing Office.
Basic Field Manual 23-6, U. S. Rifle, Caliber .30, M1917. Washington, Government Printing Office, 1943.
Basic Field Manual 23-10, U. S. Rifle, Caliber .30, M1903. Washington, Government Printing Office, 1943.
Description and Rules for the Management of the United States Magazine Rifle and Carbine, Caliber .30, Model of 1898. Washington, Government Printing Office, 1917.
Description and Rules for the Management of the United States Rifle, Caliber .30, Model of 1903. Washington, Government Printing Office, 1917.
Description and Rules for the Management of the United States Rifle, Caliber .30, Model of 1917. Washington, Government Printing Office, 1917.
Executive Documents of the House of Representatives, 1875–76. Washington, Government Printing Office.
Executive Documents of the House of Representatives, 1876–77, 1877–78, 1878–79. Washington, Government Printing Office.
Report of the Secretary of War, 1862. Washington, Government Printing Office, 1862.
Senate Documents, 1st Session, 35th Congress, 1857–58. William A. Harris, Printer, Washington, 1858.

BOOKS

Alger, Russell A.: *The Spanish-American War.* Harper & Bros., New York, 1901.
Catton, Bruce: *Mr. Lincoln's Army.* Doubleday & Company, Inc., New York, 1951.

Chapel, Charles E.: *Gun Collecting.* Coward-McCann, Inc., New York, 1939.

Chapel, Charles E.: *The Gun Collector's Handbook of Values.* Coward-McCann, Inc., New York, 1947.

Creasy, E. S.: *The Fifteen Decisive Battles of the World.* Revised and edited by R. H. Murray, Military Service Publishing Company, Harrisburg, Pennsylvania, 1943.

Davis, Tenney L.: *The Chemistry of Powder and Explosives.* J. Wiley & Sons, New York, 1943.

Gluckman, Colonel Arcadi: *United States Muskets, Rifles and Carbines.* Otto Ulbrich Company, Inc., Buffalo, New York, 1948.

Goddard, Lieutenant Colonel Calvin: *Proof Tests and Proof Marks.* The Army Ordnance Association, Washington, D. C., 1946.

Gordon, General John B.: *Reminiscences of the Civil War.* Charles Scribner's Sons, New York, 1905.

Hall, Walter P.: *World Wars and Revolutions.* D. Appleton-Century Company, New York, 1943.

Hatcher, General Julian S.: *Hatcher's Notebook.* The Stackpole Company, Harrisburg, Pennsylvania, 1947.

Hatcher, General Julian S.: *Textbook of Firearms Investigation, Identification and Evidence.* Small-Arms Technical Publishing Company, Plantersville, South Carolina, 1935.

Henry, Robert S.: *The Story of the Mexican War.* The Bobbs-Merrill Company, Inc., Indianapolis, 1950.

Hicks, John D.: *A Short History of American Democracy.* Houghton Mifflin Company, Boston, 1944.

Jacobs, James R.: *The Beginning of the U. S. Army, 1783-1812.* Princeton University Press, Princeton, New Jersey, 1947.

Johnson, Melvin M., and Haven, Charles T.: *Ammunition: Its History, Development and Use.* William Morrow & Company, New York, 1943.

Lefferts, Charles M.: *Uniforms of the American, British, French, and German Armies in the War of the American Revolution.* The New York Historical Society, New York, 1926.

Lezius, Martin: *Das Ehrenkleid des Soldaten.* Ullstein, Berlin, 1936.

Marshall, Samuel L. A.: *Men Against Fire.* Infantry Journal Press, Washington, 1947; William Morrow & Company, New York, 1947.

Sawyer, Charles W.: *Our Rifles.* Williams Book Store, Boston, 1946.

Sharpe, Philip B.: *The Rifle in America.* William Morrow & Company, New York, 1938.

Smith, W. H. B.: *A Basic Manual of Military Small Arms.* Military Service Publishing Company, Harrisburg, Pennsylvania, 1944.

Smith, W. H. B.: *Mauser Rifles and Pistols.* Military Service Publishing Company, Harrisburg, Pennsylvania, 1947.

Smith, Winston O.: *The Sharps Rifle.* William Morrow & Company, New York, 1943.

Wintringham, Tom: *The Story of Weapons and Tactics from Troy to Stalingrad.* Houghton Mifflin Company, Boston, 1943.

Index